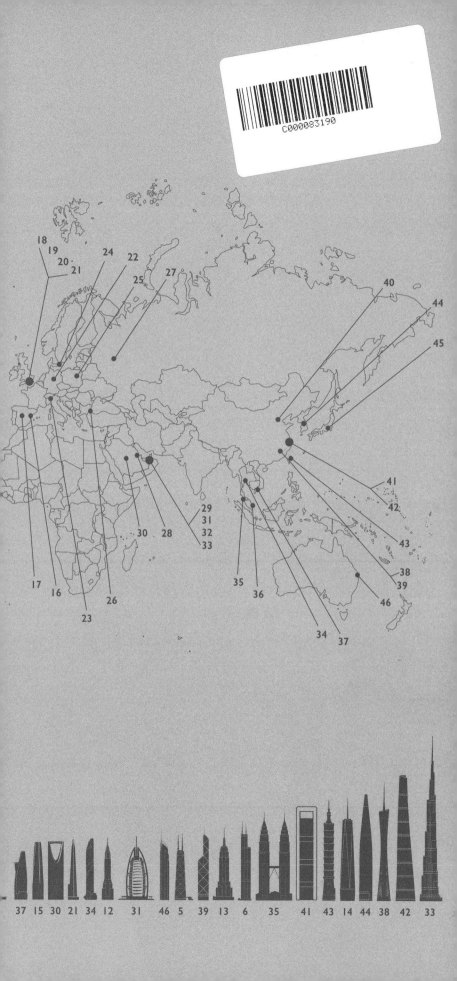

18
19
20
21
24
22
25
27
40
44
45

17
16
23
26
30
28
29
31
32
33
35
36
34
37
46
38
39

37 15 30 21 34 12 31 46 5 39 13 6 35 41 43 14 44 38 42 33

HOW TO BUILD A

SKYSCRAPER

Inspiring | Educating | Creating | Entertaining

Brimming with creative inspiration, how-to projects, and useful information to enrich your everyday life, Quarto Knows is a favourite destination for those pursuing their interests and passions. Visit our site and dig deeper with our books into your area of interest: Quarto Creates, Quarto Cooks, Quarto Homes, Quarto Lives, Quarto Drives, Quarto Explores, Quarto Gifts, or Quarto Kids.

© 2017 Quarto Publishing plc

First Published in 2017 by RotoVision,
an imprint of The Quarto Group.
The Old Brewery, 6 Blundell Street,
London N7 9BH, United Kingdom
T (0)20 7700 6700 F (02)20 7700 8066
www.QuartoKnows.com

10 9 8 7 6 5 4 3 2 1

ISBN: 978-2-88893-343-4

Publisher: Mark Searle
Editorial Director: Isheeta Mustafi
Commissioning Editor: Emily Angus
Editor: Stephen Haynes
Junior Editor: Abbie Sharman
Design Concept & Cover Design: Michelle Rowlandson
Page Design: Briony Hartley

Image credits:
Cover and opposite: © studio esinam

Printed in China

HOW TO BUILD A

SKYSCRAPER

JOHN HILL

ROTOVISION BOOKS

CONTENTS

INTRODUCTION

Why don't all skyscrapers look the same? This question may seem preposterous – silly even – but there is some logic behind it. Tall buildings are created to maximize the value of land, usually expensive land in city centres – the taller the building, the more money for the client. In order to build taller, structural engineers aim to enclose the most space with the least material, all the while bringing the forces of gravity safely to the ground and adequately resisting wind forces so users are comfortable. Architects give skyscrapers their strongest expression – their façades – yet they work within stylistic currents that root them in a particular period. The contributions of these three key players (architects, clients and engineers) ensure that each skyscraper converges on the goal of being the tallest, the most structurally efficient and the most beautiful – perfection approaching the heavens.

Yet, as the selection of skyscrapers in this book attests, variation is found all around us. Encounters with standard-issue high-rises – as in boxy, mid-century office buildings in the United States, or China's booming urbanism in this century – attest to the need for diversity in the built environment. Four general areas contribute most to a skyscraper's unique form: nature, economics, technology and aesthetics.

Nature, in the largest sense of the word, dictates the forces that any building must address, but this is especially true of skyscrapers, whose height makes them more vulnerable to natural extremes than other buildings. Every skyscraper exists in a physical place, and each place has its distinctive climate, soil conditions, seismic concerns, wind patterns and so on; all contribute to how a skyscraper is designed, engineered and built.

Nature may rule, but all skyscrapers exist to make money and each particular site yields a particular economic 'sweet spot': too short and the building will not pay for itself; too tall and it will cost too much up front or sit partially empty for years; just right and it meets the economic demands it was made for, be it for a specific tenant or a particular function.

Height is also a function of the technology available at any given time. Just consider how the elevator pushed buildings above the heights people were willing to climb by stairs, or how steel framing took over the structural role from heavy, load-bearing exterior walls. Advances in computers make increasingly taller buildings easier to engineer, while advances in materials (such as high-strength concrete) make them feasible physically.

Last but not least, skyscrapers have a presence within the public realm and on a city skyline that is shaped by a combination of height, form and skin – aesthetics, in other words. Clients want a distinctive tower to attract tenants, while architects strive for beauty and a lasting legacy; repeating designs is anathema to these goals.

With this context in mind, this book describes how and why 46 skyscrapers – placed in order from west to east, following the migration of tall buildings over the last 100-plus years – look the way they do. Each building is the product of its particular circumstances, and this book reveals the stories behind their fruition.

TRANSAMERICA PYRAMID

LOCATION: San Francisco, CA, USA | **COMPLETION:** 1972
HEIGHT: 260m (853ft) | **STOREYS:** 48 | **PRIMARY FUNCTION:** Offices
OWNER/DEVELOPER: Transamerica Corporation, AEGON USA
ARCHITECT: William L Pereira & Associates | **STRUCTURAL ENGINEER:**
Chin & Hensolt | **KEY FACTS:** The tallest building in San Francisco
until the completion of Salesforce Tower in 2017.

Pyramid as Skyscraper

The pyramids of Egypt are some of the oldest and most impressive structures on earth, but their pointed forms are a rarity when it comes to modern skyscrapers. For Transamerica executive John Beckett and his architect William Pereira, there was some logic in the form, primarily in the way it allowed more sunlight to hit the streets so the building cast a smaller shadow on its surroundings. And it certainly didn't hurt that the pyramid shape circumvented the city's building regulations, which prescribed a ratio between height and floor area. The Transamerica Pyramid cast a distinctive profile on the skyline, helping to turn the little-known holding company into a major insurance provider.

Resistance

Although San Francisco – home to the former hippie enclave of Haight–Ashbury and to a large LGBT population – is one of the most socially liberal US cities, in terms of its architecture it is very conservative.

Beckett and Pereira confronted this once their plans became known publicly in 1969, the same year construction started. A *Newsweek* article described the tower as 'wrong in any city' and protests tried to halt the project. But three years later it was completed and since then it has been a symbol of the city as much as of Transamerica Corporation, which moved its headquarters out of the building in 1989 but retains an image of the tower in its logo.

The tower's distinctive top is formed by its unoccupied aluminium crown and parts of the core that continue past the tapered sides.

BUILDING AND STRUCTURE

Structure

The pyramidal form lowers the building's centre of gravity and provides the tower with structural stability in geologically active San Francisco. Designed, like all towers in the city, to resist an 8.3-magnitude earthquake, the building's most overt elements of lateral and torsional (twisting) stability are found at the square base: 20 three-storey isosceles tetrahedrons that cap an arcade on all four sides. The structure above consists of the leaning steel external frame, four inner frames up to the 17th floor, two inner frames up to the 45th floor, and concrete floors. Below ground are three basement levels, while the entire building sits on a 2.75m (9ft) deep reinforced concrete mat that was famously poured over the course of one day. The tower was put to the test in October 1989, when the 7.1-magnitude Loma Prieta earthquake struck; the building swayed up to 30cm (1ft) for nearly a minute but survived without sustaining any damage.

Exterior

The muted façades of the skyscraper are covered in precast concrete panels with a white quartz finish. Most of these panels, which are reinforced at each floor to allow for lateral movement, frame the 3,678 windows that reach from the 6th floor to the 48th-floor conference room. Since the pyramidal form does not easily enable window-washing rigs to descend the exterior, the windows pivot so they can be washed from the inside.

Projecting from the 29th floor to the top floor on two sides of the tower are 'wings' that house two lifts on the east and a stairwell and smoke tower on the west. Above them is a decorative aluminium spire – at 64.6m (212ft) the equivalent of a 20-storey building – which brings the pyramidal form to its satisfying resolution.

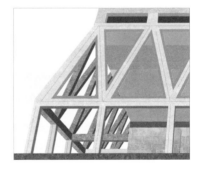

The tapered tower flares out at the base, where three-storey bracing stabilizes the building during earthquakes.

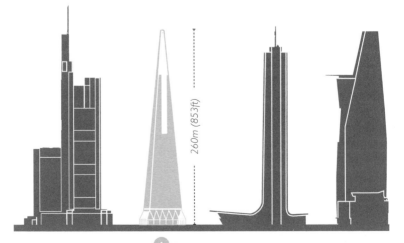

260m (853ft)

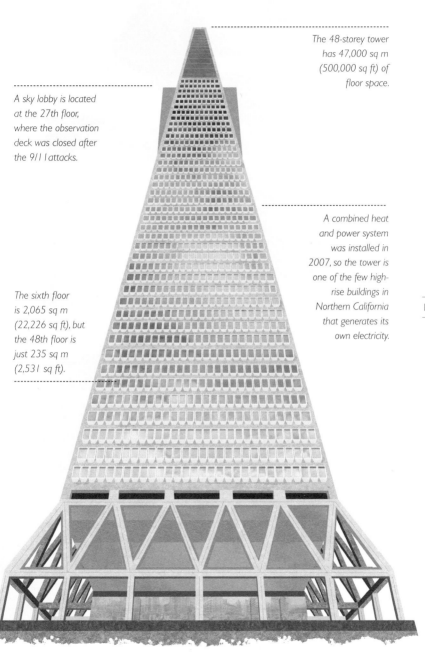

The 48-storey tower has 47,000 sq m (500,000 sq ft) of floor space.

A sky lobby is located at the 27th floor, where the observation deck was closed after the 9/11 attacks.

A combined heat and power system was installed in 2007, so the tower is one of the few high-rise buildings in Northern California that generates its own electricity.

The sixth floor is 2,065 sq m (22,226 sq ft), but the 48th floor is just 235 sq m (2,531 sq ft).

RAINIER TOWER

LOCATION: Seattle, WA, USA | COMPLETION: 1977 | HEIGHT: 157m (514ft) | STOREYS: 31 excluding pedestal | PRIMARY FUNCTION: Offices | OWNER/DEVELOPER: Rainier Bank, Unico Properties ARCHITECT: Minoru Yamasaki Associates, NBBJ | STRUCTURAL ENGINEER: Skilling, Helle, Christiansen, Robertson KEY FACTS: Called 'The Beaver Building' for its tapered pedestal. With its pedestal, the tower is the equivalent of 42 storeys tall.

Minoru Yamasaki

It is unfortunate that the legacy of Japanese-American architect Minoru Yamasaki is tied to two projects that were destroyed under extraordinary circumstances: the Pruitt-Igoe housing project in St Louis was demolished only 14 years after its 1956 completion due to decay and crime; and terrorists flew two aeroplanes into New York's Twin Towers as part of the attacks of 11 September 2001, killing more than 2,600 people in the buildings and destroying the architect's most famous project. Before and after the completion of the Twin Towers in 1973, Yamasaki had designed other skyscrapers –including Rainier Tower in the city where he was born – that exhibit his distinctive pinstriped modernism.

Downtown Seattle

Rainier Tower was the second tall building that Yamasaki designed for Downtown Seattle. In 1964 he completed the 20-storey IBM Building, whose striped exterior walls and arched colonnade foreshadowed the towers he completed in Lower Manhattan 10 years later. IBM sits diagonally opposite Rainier Tower, which was commissioned in 1972 for two clients: University Properties, Inc. (Unico), which was also his client at IBM; and National Bank of Commerce, which would change its name to Rainier Bank and for which Yamasaki had developed schematic plans on another site.

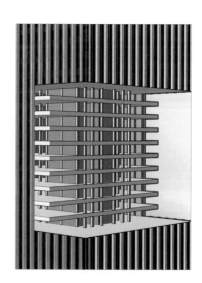

Although the tapered base gives the impression of a reinforced concrete tower, the core is framed in structural steel.

BUILDING AND STRUCTURE

Façades

The dialogue between Yamasaki's two Downtown Seattle towers is most evident in their square footprints and their vertically striped cladding. The first feature stemmed from the rational process of designing office spaces around central cores, while the second was based on the architect's dislike of all-glass towers. After subtracting spandrel panels and column covers, he asserted that all-glass buildings give about 60 per cent of their façade area over to windows. With his towers he aimed for 30 per cent, which would provide views outside but also a feeling of security and a frame from which to look out. Yamasaki achieved this relatively low percentage by providing narrowly spaced vertical panels, which also had the effect of accentuating the verticality of his towers. Rainier Tower's façade is clad in glass and aluminium, the latter in the form of alternating wide and narrow stripes.

Pedestal

If Rainier Tower existed solely as 29 floors of offices covered in stripes of aluminium, it would be forgotten easily. But, to realize his goal of giving over as much of the site as possible to open space – about 75 per cent, comprising a retail podium with a landscaped roof – Yamasaki lifted up the office floors on a fluted, 11-storey concrete pedestal. This gesture also raised those floors above their neighbours to give the tenants views of Elliott Bay.

The pedestal is made of reinforced concrete faced with tiles.

The thick, reinforced-concrete walls of the base carry the steel perimeter frame of the tower above, which acts like a building-sized Vierendeel truss. Although the appears precarious – like a tree half-felled by a beaver – the structural engineers (now Magnusson Klemencic Associates) contend that it is one of the most earthquake-resistant buildings *ever* built – which is important given the Seattle region's vulnerability to seismic activity.

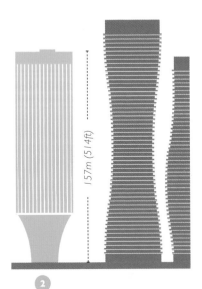

157m (514ft)

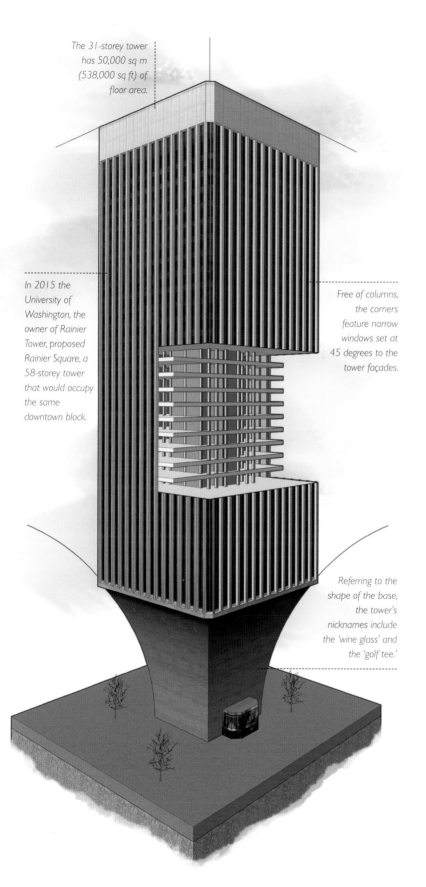

The 31-storey tower has 50,000 sq m (538,000 sq ft) of floor area.

In 2015 the University of Washington, the owner of Rainier Tower, proposed Rainier Square, a 58-storey tower that would occupy the same downtown block.

Free of columns, the corners feature narrow windows set at 45 degrees to the tower façades.

Referring to the shape of the base, the tower's nicknames include the 'wine glass' and the 'golf tee.'

FOUNTAIN PLACE

LOCATION: Dallas, TX, USA | COMPLETION: 1986 | HEIGHT: 220m (720ft) | STOREYS: 60 | PRIMARY FUNCTION: Offices | OWNER/DEVELOPER: Goddard Investment Group; Criswell Development Company, Campeau Corporation | ARCHITECT: I M Pei & Partners, Architectural Consulting Services Inc. | STRUCTURAL ENGINEER: CBM Engineers | KEY FACTS: Was to have been the first of two matching towers – the second was never built. Fountain Place won the 25-Year Award from Texas Society of Architects in 2011.

Site History

When Fountain Place was developed in the early 1980s by Dallas's Criswell and Canada's Campeau, Allied Bank Tower was the first of three planned phases for the 2.3-hectare (5.8-acre) site. The second phase would have been a twin 60-storey tower – rotated 90 degrees from the first – and the third, a 300-room hotel. The recession subsequent to the 1986 completion of the first tower meant it would stand alone – yet almost immediately it became a Dallas landmark. The tower changed hands numerous times (most recently in 2014) and eventually took on the name Fountain Place due to the popular plaza that Dan Kiley designed at its base, with hundreds of bubbling fountains.

Henry Cobb

Allied Bank Tower was one of three office towers designed by Henry Cobb of I M Pei & Partners (now Pei Cobb Freed & Partners) for Dallas in the 1970s and 1980s. Each tower departed from the convention of rectangular boxes to overcome what Cobb saw as their 'homogenizing' effect. One was diamond-shaped, another was triangular, while this tower for Allied Bank adopted a combination of prismatic forms.

About 24,000 glass panes make up the 6,500 window units covering the tower.

Building Form

Geometrically, the Fountain Place tower is composed of four shapes: a cube at its base, a rhomboid accompanied by two right-triangle tetrahedrons in the middle and a triangular prism on top. Yet Cobb conceptualized the final ten-sided form as being carved from a single rectilinear block: he extruded the square plan to the maximum height allowed by law for flight paths and then carved away at it with prisms in plan and section. The effect of carving is most pronounced at ground level, where four-storey-high, angled openings at opposite corners (aligned with the rhomboid above) allow the plaza to continue beneath the tower and provide access to the equally tall lobby.

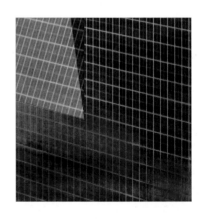

BUILDING AND STRUCTURE

Façade

For Cobb, the 'perfection' of the building's geometry was planar, so it required a completely flat façade that appeared solid. To achieve this, reflective green glass was selected for the curtain wall. Its 6,500 window units are held in place on the inside with silver mullions and on the outside with structural silicone; the 46,450 sq m (500,000 sq ft) installation was considered at the time to be the largest silicone curtain wall ever erected.

Structure

Since expressed structure would conflict with the intention of geometric perfection, the 17,690 tonnes 17,410 tons) of steel holding up the tower were placed behind the glass façade. Amazingly, more than half of the tower's steel tonnage occupies the first five floors. From the 5th floor to the 44th, the structure is composed of a megatruss, whose components include columns, 7.5-storey-tall diagonals, and full-floor Vierendeel trusses that act as horizontal chord members. At the top are an eight-storey-high welded frame and a welded triangular hat truss, which resist torsional (twisting) forces acting on the building. The structural system eliminates the need for internal bracing and allows the weight of the building to be carried by only eight columns at the base – freeing up space for even more of the building's namesake water features.

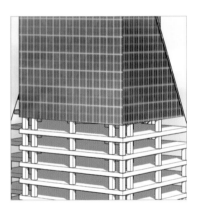

Given the tower's tapering form, the construction time ranged from one floor per week to one per day.

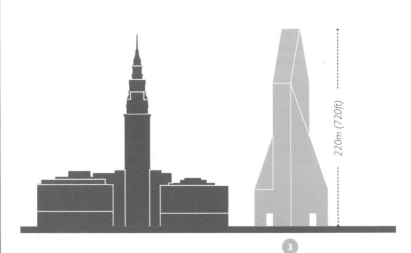

220m (720ft)

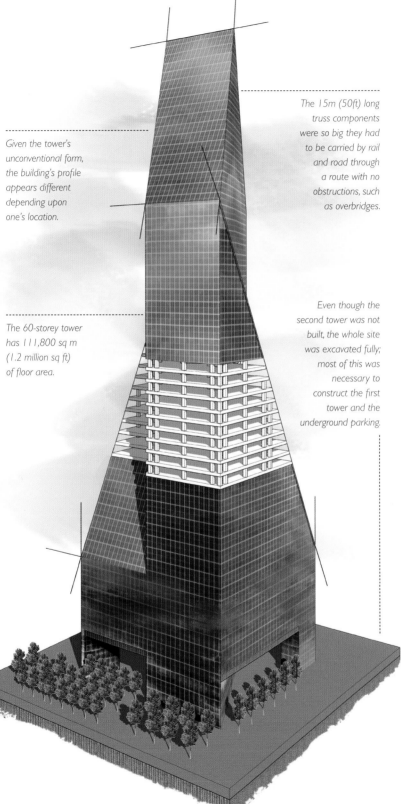

Given the tower's unconventional form, the building's profile appears different depending upon one's location.

The 60-storey tower has 111,800 sq m (1.2 million sq ft) of floor area.

The 15m (50ft) long truss components were so big they had to be carried by rail and road through a route with no obstructions, such as overbridges.

Even though the second tower was not built, the whole site was excavated fully; most of this was necessary to construct the first tower and the underground parking.

TRIBUNE TOWER

Location: Chicago, IL, USA | **Completion:** 1925 | **Height:** 141m (463ft) | **Storeys:** 34 | **Primary Function:** Offices | **Owner/ Developer:** CIM Group, Golub & Company; Tribune Media, Tribune Publishing | **Architect:** Hood and Howells | **Structural Engineer:** Henry J Burt | **Key Facts:** The tower is the eighth home for the *Chicago Tribune* newspaper, founded in 1847.

Historical Context

Business was great for the *Chicago Tribune* in the second decade of the 20th century: the newspaper's circulation and advertising receipts doubled. Having outgrown its turn-of-the-century building in the Loop (Chicago's central business district), the *Tribune* looked further afield for the site of its new home. In 1919 the company bought a parcel of land north of the Chicago River on Michigan Avenue, which would be connected to the Loop by a double-decker bridge the following year. The *Tribune* immediately constructed a building for its printing press on the east side of the block, reserving the west side for an office tower to be designed by the winner of an architectural competition.

The Competition

Editors Robert McCormick and Joseph Patterson headed the *Tribune*, and together they developed the idea for the competition, which would be advertised in the newspaper's local,

national and European editions. The June 1922 announcement (coinciding with the newspaper's 75th anniversary), combined with an unheard-of $100,000 US purse – $50,000 going to the winner – led to the submission of 263 entries from three continents. The deadline for entries was 1 November, but a 30-day grace period was allowed for foreign architects. Eliel Saarinen's entry, which arrived from Finland on 29 November, was the favourite of Alfred Granger, the sole architect on the five-person jury. But the four jurors from the *Tribune* (who included McCormick and Patterson) had already made up their minds, relegating Saarinen's soaring design to second place.

The offices of McCormick and Patterson sat on the top floor, with stairs leading up to a roof terrace behind the neo-Gothic flying buttresses.

BUILDING AND STRUCTURE

A Nod to the Past

One day after the receipt of Saarinen's entry, McCormick sent a telegram to the winners, John Mead Howells and Raymond Hood. If the competing architects had been hoping for a modern choice that would point the way forward for the design of skyscrapers, the *Tribune*'s selection was the reverse: a step back in stylistic terms. Although framed in steel, the highly ornamented stone exterior resembled a French Gothic cathedral, most overtly in the flying buttresses surrounding the octagonal crown.

Foundations

As befits a daily paper, construction of the tower could not be allowed to adversely impact the neighbouring printing plant; this had to stay in operation until the tower was finished in 1925, at which time its facilities would be extended into the tower's base. The situation was complicated by the fact that an extension to the plant overlapped the tower's footprint. New girders and caissons had to be installed below the extension at the same time as caissons for the tower were sunk 36.5m (120ft) deep for the tower; workers checked sensors intermittently to ensure that settling did not throw the printing presses out of alignment.

Fragments of famous international buildings – such as the Berlin Wall, the Great Wall of China and the Pyramid of Cheops) – are embedded into the base of the limestone façade on the north side of the tower.

A Change of Plan

The structural steel frame now began to rise from the foundation, but after the steel had been ordered the *Tribune* decided it wanted a taller building. Working with Hood and Howells, they inserted four more floors in the middle of the building to gain a further 17m (56ft). These extra floors gave the building more vertical thrust, even though the Indiana limestone panels hung on the steel frame gave the appearance of a solid, carved mass. Nearly a century after its competition, the Tribune Tower is an icon known around the world – just what the original client wanted.

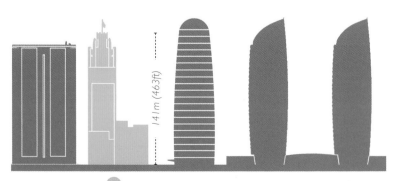

141m (463ft)

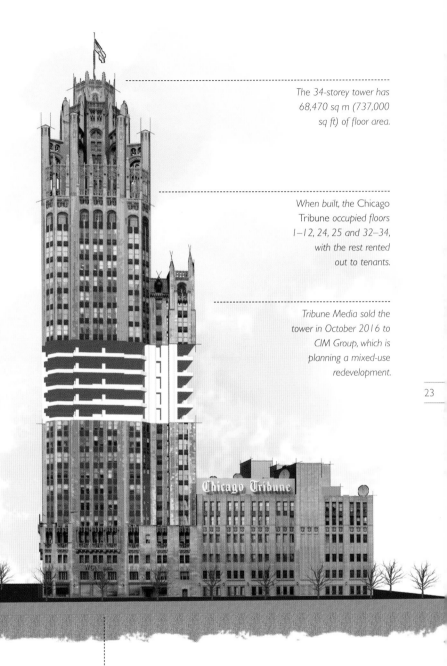

The 34-storey tower has 68,470 sq m (737,000 sq ft) of floor area.

When built, the Chicago Tribune occupied floors 1–12, 24, 25 and 32–34, with the rest rented out to tenants.

Tribune Media sold the tower in October 2016 to CIM Group, which is planning a mixed-use redevelopment.

23

22,900 cu m (808,700 cu ft) of soil were excavated during the tower's construction, with caissons ranging in diameter from 1.2m (4ft) to 2.9m (9½ft).

JOHN HANCOCK CENTER

Location: Chicago, IL, USA | **Completion:** 1969 | **Height:** 344m (1,128ft) | **Storeys:** 100 | **Primary Functions:** Residential, offices **Owner/Developer:** Hearn Company, Jerry Wolman Associates **Architect:** Skidmore, Owings & Merrill (SOM) | **Structural Engineer:** SOM | **Key Facts:** Affectionately known as 'Big John' since its completion. The world's first trussed-tube or braced-tube structure.

Historical Background

Chicago is considered the birthplace of the skyscraper, on the basis of the 1884 completion of the 10-storey Home Insurance Building. Although short by later standards, this design by William LeBaron Jenney incorporated the world's first steel-frame construction with non-load-bearing exterior walls. This method was advanced in the city in the following decades, leading to such notable structures as the 34-storey Tribune Tower (page 20), but after that tower's completion in 1923 the city effectively capped the height of tall buildings at around 20 storeys. It was not until the mid-1950s that height restrictions were eliminated and skyscrapers rose again in the Windy City.

Mixed Uses

Chicago's towers congregated in and around the Loop, but developer Jerry Wolman wanted to build two towers – one for offices and one for apartments – on North Michigan Avenue, about 1.6km (1 mile) north of the Loop. He approached SOM with the project in 1964, and their architect Bruce Graham started by proposing two towers on the nearly full-block site a couple of blocks from the Water Tower, the famous survivor of the Great Fire of 1871. Wolman went bankrupt and John Hancock Mutual Life Insurance Company took over in 1967.

The top floors feature mechanical and broadcasting services, a glowing lantern, a restaurant and an observation deck that added a 'TILT' facility in 2014, where visitors stand on a platform that tilts outside the building at 30 degrees.

BUILDING AND STRUCTURE

One Tower Becomes Two

Concerned that apartment residents would look into the windows of the office tower and vice-versa, Graham and SOM structural engineer Fazlur Khan proposed a single building: a 100-storey skyscraper with apartments lifted above the offices for better views. Commercial space and parking would comprise the first half-dozen floors, while a restaurant, observation deck and broadcasting facilities sat at the top. To zip residents to and from their apartments, one of the first express elevator systems was implemented, with a sky lobby where apartment dwellers could switch between express and local elevators.

Tapered Form

Since office spaces can work with deep floor plates but apartments need to be shallow for natural light, the stacking of these two main uses led to a tapered form. From the ground floor to the top floor, the square footage of the rectangular plan shrinks by more than 60 per cent. Although it makes leasing the office spaces and laying out apartments a bit trickier, the tapered shape has the benefit of cutting down on the 'sail factor' caused by winds from Lake Michigan.

Braced-Tube Construction

The stacked programme and tapered form led Khan to implement one of the most innovative and influential structural systems in the short history of skyscrapers. Buildings with exterior bracing had existed as early as the 19th century, but Khan eliminated intermediate columns between the exterior frame and the core to create the first braced-tube building – another Chicago innovation. The diagonal bracing results in column/

floor intersections every three floors, and with the tapered form this meant that floor-to-floor heights varied – but the strong resistance to lateral forces makes living so high comfortable (there is no perceptible sway) and the amount of steel used is reduced to the equivalent of a 45-storey building. Not bad for a 100-storey skyscraper that started as two buildings.

The façade is covered in black anodized aluminium and bronze glass, with black louvres at the mechanical floors.

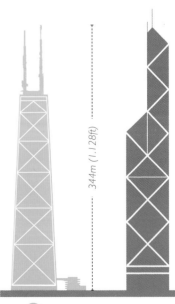

344m (1,128ft)

The antennas reach a height of 457m (1,499ft), the highest allowed by the Federal Aviation Administration at the time.

The 100-storey tower has 260,000 sq m (2.8 million sq ft) of floor space.

In 1999 the John Hancock Center received the American Institute of Architects' 25-Year Award.

An external parking ramp delivers cars to the parking garage located in the base of the skyscraper.

WILLIS TOWER

Location: Chicago, IL, USA | **Completion:** 1974 | **Height:** 442m (1,451ft) | **Storeys:** 108 | **Primary Function:** Offices | **Owner/ Developer:** Blackstone Group; Sears, Roebuck and Company **Architect:** Skidmore, Owings & Merrill (SOM) | **Structural Engineer:** SOM | **Key Facts:** The world's tallest building from 1974 until 1998. The world's first bundled-tube structure.

Graham and Khan

In 1969, SOM's Bruce Graham and Fazlur Khan had created one of the most distinctive and influential modern skyscrapers, the John Hancock Center (page 24), when the architect and engineer fused their respective disciplines in an expression both rational and dramatic. Following that, the pair was tasked with designing a home for the 10,000 employees of department store chain Sears, Roebuck and Company, who were then situated in an early 20th-century complex on the city's West Side. The result would become the world's tallest building and another dose of rational drama.

Planning

In the same year that Graham and Khan wrapped up the Hancock, Sears hired New York interior design firm Environetics to determine the corporation's space-planning needs. After interviewing nearly one hundred managers they determined a target area of 186,000 sq m (2 million sq ft), with half as much again to allow for growth and an ideal floor plate of 4,645 sq m (50,000 sq ft). SOM had to turn these numbers and other detailed requirements into a building as unique on the city's skyline as the Hancock.

From Sears to Willis

Sears's projected growth never materialized, so in the mid-1990s the corporation moved to the suburbs. Regardless, the iconic building continued to be known as the Sears Tower until 2009, when London's Willis Group Holdings leased only 13,000 sq m (140,000 sq ft) in the roughly 371,600 sq m (4 million sq ft) tower and gained naming rights. To many it is still the Sears Tower, harking back to a time when 'world's tallest' was associated with American buildings.

In 2009 SOM was hired to add 'The Ledge,' glass boxes cantilevered from the 103rd floor, offering a vertiginous thrill to tourists visiting the Skydeck.

BUILDING AND STRUCTURE

Bundled Tubes

With a 1.2-hectare (3-acre) site just east of the Chicago River in the Loop, SOM worked up nearly 50 schemes, ranging from 60 to 120 storeys. An anecdote often repeated claims that Graham bunched some cigarettes in his hand, a few of them sticking up higher than the others, and asked Khan if it would work. That moment pushed Khan to devise the first bundled-tube structure. Nine rigid, steel-frame tubes – each one 23m (75ft) square with perimeter columns every 4.6m (15ft) – make up the base of the tower, creating a 4,700 sq m (50,625 sq ft) footprint on target with the planning needs. Seven of the nine tubes terminate at the 50th, 66th and 90th floors to create the 110-storey skyscraper's distinctive asymmetrical profile and to minimize the impact of lateral winds on the upper floors.

Bundling the Bundles

But how to unite structurally what were in effect nine separate towers? In much the same way as Graham's fist held the cigarettes together, Khan and his team devised two-storey belt trusses that wrap the exterior to connect the tubes together. These occur about halfway up the nine-square base; at the levels where the bundles stop; and at the very top. In all cases they coincide with mechanical floors so the diagonal trusses do not affect any office floors.

Vertical Circulation

With 10,000 Sears employees and another 6,000 tenants, a lot of lifts were needed – 104 to be precise – 14 of them double-deckers, carrying passengers to sky lobbies on the 33rd/34th and 66th/67th floors where they could transfer to local elevators. The tower's stepped form makes it easy to terminate elevators and shrink the core, but at least one lift travels top to bottom, zipping visitors to the 103rd-floor observation deck in just 60 seconds.

In early 2017 the Blackstone Group announced a $500 million plan to transform the plaza around the base into a retail structure with a green roof.

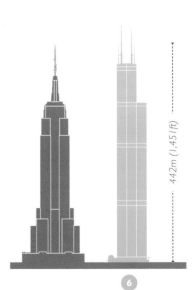

442m (1,451ft)

If the two antennas atop the roof counted in the tower's height, Willis Tower would be 527m (1,729ft) tall.

The façades wrapping the building are made of black aluminium with energy-efficient bronze-tinted glass.

With the bundled-tube structure, there are no columns between perimeter and core.

Blackstone Group purchased Willis Tower in 2015 for $1.3 billion US.

TERMINAL TOWER

LOCATION: Cleveland, OH, USA | COMPLETION: 1928
HEIGHT: 216m (708ft) | STOREYS: 52 | PRIMARY FUNCTION: Offices
OWNER/DEVELOPER: Oris Paxton Van Sweringen and Mantis James Van
Sweringen | ARCHITECT: Graham, Anderson, Probst & White
STRUCTURAL ENGINEER: H D Jouett | KEY FACTS: The tallest building
outside New York City from 1928 until 1953. Tower added to the National
Register of Historic Places in 1976.

Historical Context

Public and private interests collided in 1900s Cleveland when brothers Oris and Mantis Van Sweringen wanted commuter trains to move people to and from their suburban developments but were unable to use the existing tracks and depot near Lake Erie. The brothers persuaded voters to let them build a new railway terminal on land they owned on the southwest corner of Public Square in Downtown Cleveland, as an alternative to the new lakefront station envisioned in the 1903 Group Plan developed by Daniel H Burnham. Given the go-ahead, the Van Sweringens built the terminal and capped it with a seven-building project with the landmark 52-storey Terminal Tower as its centrepiece.

Terminal Group

The Van Sweringens hired Chicago's Graham, Anderson, Probst & White (GAP&W) – the successor of Burnham's firm – to design what is now known as Tower City Center, though in their first scheme, in 1919, no tower was present. It was not until 1925, one year after an amendment was passed allowing tall buildings in the city, that the brothers announced a project that would be for Cleveland what the Woolworth Building was for New York. Flanking the tower on the east and west were, respectively, a new department store and a just-built hotel (by GAP&W) that was made part of the complex, while a trio of 18-storey office buildings were built on the blocks to the south. Office tenants moved into the tower in 1928, when it gained some attention as the tallest building outside New York City, and the whole assemblage was dedicated in June 1930.

The tower is positioned at 45 degrees to Public Square and the flanking buildings that are part of the Terminal project.

BUILDING AND STRUCTURE

Tower on a Terminal

Naturally, the underground tracks and platforms were a driving force in what happened above, be it the spacing of columns or the layout of public concourses that linked the complex together below street level. The introduction of the tower threw a kink into the station plans, in part because of the tower's central core, but also because of the columns that needed to knit themselves between the tracks. The architects capably addressed these and other issues, but construction on the station could not start until 1928, after the tower had been completed.

A flagpole atop the cupola pushes the tower's height to 235m (771ft).

Construction

Given the various types of clays below the complex, the 58,000-tonne (57,000-ton) tower was built on 16 caissons, 3m (10ft) in diameter, carried down more than 60m (200ft) to firm shale. The tower had its own piles, separate from the station's, in order to reduce vibration from trains. Foundation work started in January 1926 and was completed by July thanks to 250 men working around the clock in alternating eight-hour shifts. By comparison, the steel structure was relatively easy, topping off in August 1927.

Cupola

Although Terminal Tower is considered a 52-storey building, the highest accessible floor is the observation deck on 42. Above it are some mechanical floors inside a cupola that resembles McKim, Mead & White's Municipal Building in New York. This decorative top pushed the tower higher and ensured that it became the symbol of Cleveland – a distinction it still retains, even though the decline in rail traffic over the past century meant that most of the tracks were turned into car parking.

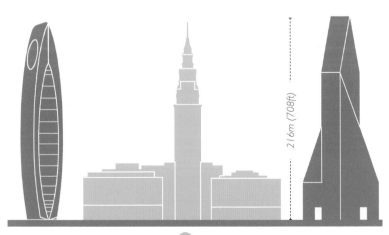

216m (708ft)

7

The 52-storey tower has 53,600 sq m (577,000 sq ft) of floor space.

The tower features approximately 2,200 windows, all of them replaced with double-pane, insulated glazing during a restoration this century.

The tower's floors are served by 23 lifts.

Around 2,000 buildings were destroyed and 15,000 people relocated to make way for the whole Terminal project.

ONE PPG PLACE

LOCATION: Pittsburgh, PA, USA | COMPLETION: 1984 | HEIGHT: 194m (635ft) | STOREYS: 40 | PRIMARY FUNCTION: Offices | OWNER/ DEVELOPER: PPG Industries | ARCHITECT: Johnson/Burgee Architects STRUCTURAL ENGINEER: Leslie E Robertson Associates (LERA) KEY FACTS: The tower is one of six buildings that make up PPG Place, the headquarters of the Pittsburgh Plate Glass Company.

Urban Renewal

Pittsburgh underwent many dramatic changes in the 20th century as it shifted from a place of industry (steel) to, like other cities in the United States, one of finance and the service sector. Today the Golden Triangle – bounded by the Monongahela, Ohio and Allegheny Rivers and the Crosstown Expressway – serves as Pittsburgh's central business district, but in the 19th century it was where the Pittsburgh Plate Glass Company (PPG) started and where its factories were located. When, between 1979 and 1984, PPG built its corporate headquarters, it gave the city a tower for its skyline and a plaza with a fountain for its public realm, both located at the heart of the six-building complex. As part of the city's Downtown Development Strategy, the project links the historic Market Square to the north with developments overlooking the Monongahela to the south.

Historical Precedents

PPG hired Philip Johnson, who was then in partnership with John Burgee, to design the tower and the low-rise buildings surrounding it. Johnson was a chameleon when it came to architectural styles, and in the 1980s his buildings were firmly entrenched in Postmodernism, which looked to history for formal inspiration. His most famous design of this period was the AT&T – now Sony – Building, a granite-clad tower in Midtown Manhattan with a distinctive Chippendale top. Johnson designed PPG at the same time, but he was required, for obvious reasons, to build in glass, not stone.

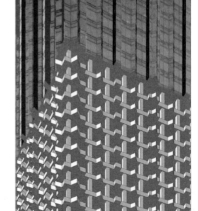

The complex shape of the curtain wall required numerous slab projections to accommodate the vertical mullions.

BUILDING AND STRUCTURE

Inspiration from the Past

Johnson sought inspiration from old buildings near and far, particularly from the Cathedral of Learning at the University of Pittsburgh and the 19th-century Victoria Tower at the Houses of Parliament in London. The result is a spiky neo-Gothic design covered in a glass whose darkness conveys the solidity of stone.

The smaller buildings that surround the tower are also capped by spiky glass turrets that reiterate the neo-Gothic motif.

Glass

The 40-storey One PPG Place and its companions are sheathed entirely – all 19,750 panes – in PPG's reflective Solarban 550 Twindow glazing. The high number is due in large part to the articulation of the curtain wall in plan: the vertical piers of Gothic inspiration are detailed as squared and angled glass projections. Therefore glass reflects glass as well as its surroundings, turning the building into a large-scale advertisement for PPG and its products.

The glass was manufactured in Crystal City (the Missouri town was founded in the 19th century explicitly for glass production, due to its silica deposits) and then transported to Ford City, Pennsylvania, where the panes were transformed into insulated glazing units. The panes are held in place by anodized aluminium frames – 175 different cross sections were needed for the neo-Gothic exterior. The light-coloured frames contrast with the dark glass to give the tower and its companion buildings a cartoonish appearance, with the frames outlining the lines of the piers and the individual floors.

The most striking aspect of Johnson's design is the way glass is used also for the 231 spires that project past the roof of each building, most dramatically at the top of the tower, where the corners extend the equivalent of eight storeys to be visible from all over the city.

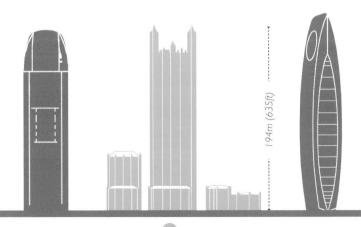

194m (635ft)

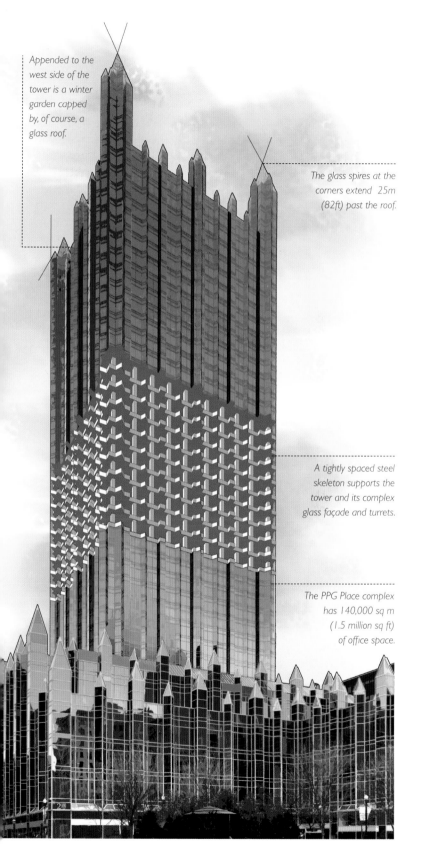

Appended to the west side of the tower is a winter garden capped by, of course, a glass roof.

The glass spires at the corners extend 25m (82ft) past the roof.

39

A tightly spaced steel skeleton supports the tower and its complex glass façade and turrets.

The PPG Place complex has 140,000 sq m (1.5 million sq ft) of office space.

ABSOLUTE TOWERS

LOCATION: Mississauga, Ontario, Canada | COMPLETION: 2012
HEIGHT: Tower 1: 176m (576ft); Tower 2: 158m (518ft) | STOREYS: Tower
1: 56; Tower 2: 50 | PRIMARY FUNCTION: Residential | OWNER/DEVELOPER:
Cityzen Development Group, Fernbrook Homes | ARCHITECT: MAD
Architects, Burka Architects | STRUCTURAL ENGINEER: Sigmund Soudack
& Associates | KEY FACTS: The 'twin' towers won the 2012 Emporis
Skyscraper Award as best new skyscraper of the year.

Mississauga

It is safe to say that before the completion of the Absolute Towers, few people outside Canada were familiar with Mississauga. Although larger in population than Vancouver, Mississauga's location within the Toronto metropolitan area means it was a relative unknown – even the airport within Mississauga's borders is named Toronto Pearson. The 'twin' twisting towers designed by Chinese architect Ma Yansong of MAD Architects put the city on the map.

Design Competition

Mississauga's own version of the 'Bilbao effect' – the establishment of a landmark building in the hope of boosting a city's economy – started when the city and developers Cityzen and Fernbrook, working in a public–private partnership, decided to hold a design competition for a tower as part of a larger residential development on a prominent, centrally located site. Competitions for residential developments in North America are rare, and nearly a hundred designs were submitted. Six finalists were voted on and MAD Architects' organic design came out on top.

Building Form

Ma Yansong wanted to introduce nature into the project through what he described as 'beautiful curves', though he did not intend the public's affectionate nickname for the project: 'Marilyn Monroe'. The curves are created by rotating each elliptical floor plan between one and eight degrees, with the greatest amount of rotation, and therefore the most dramatic turns, located in the tower's midsection. After the first tower's apartments sold out in just one weekend, the developers moved forward quickly on a second tower, which Ma designed more like a sister than a twin. Six storeys shorter, the second tower's elliptical plans rotate four degrees at each level.

Rooftop mechanical equipment is covered by glass walls that glow at night.

BUILDING AND STRUCTURE

Structure

Turning MAD's flowing design into feasible apartments and buildable structures was the biggest post-competition challenge. Columns following the rotation of the tower would have enabled unit plans to be repeated from floor to floor, but that was eschewed in favour of a grid of load-bearing concrete walls extending from the rectangular concrete core. This meant that unit plans required finessing at each floor, but the concrete walls, which address gravitational and lateral loads, simply extended or contracted in plan relative to the elliptical footprint.

Aerodynamics

The towers' sultry forms have the added benefit of being naturally aerodynamic. Regardless of direction, the helicoidal forms dissipate winds to reduce the lateral forces acting on the building. These reduced loads mean extra comfort for residents in the balconies ringing the towers.

Balconies

While the continuous balconies give every resident an outdoor space, they caused some challenges in regard to thermal bridging. To keep heat and cold from transferring to the interior via the concrete slabs, a proprietary detail was developed with a thermal break and an insulated soffit at, respectively, the base and top of each exterior wall. Yet the balconies have a couple of other benefits: they shade the apartments from the summer sun, and their pointed shapes accentuate the twists of the towers and the changing appearance of the space between them.

The four-degree rotation of the shorter, second tower is accentuated by the articulation of portions of the guardrails with translucent glass.

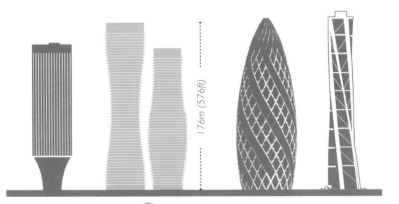

176m (576ft)

9

The 50-storey Tower 2 contains 35,380 sq m (380,800 sq ft) of floor area.

The 56-storey Tower 1 contains 40,070 sq m (432,000 sq ft) of floor area.

43

Innovation extended to the builders, who had to develop a new formwork system that climbed and rotated as the building grew.

The first tower (right) rotates a total of 209 degrees, while the second one cumulatively rotates 200 degrees.

FLATIRON BUILDING

Location: New York City, USA | **Completion:** 1902 | **Height:** 87m (285ft) | **Storeys:** 21 | **Primary Function:** Offices | **Owner/Developer:** George A Fuller Construction Company | **Architect:** Daniel H Burnham | **Structural Engineer:** George A Fuller Construction Company | **Key Facts:** Originally known as the Fuller Building for its client and builder, but renamed for its distinctive triangular shape.

George A Fuller

In 1882, architect George Allon Fuller started his eponymous company in Chicago, with the twist that he would focus entirely on construction – and not design. His embrace of the then-novel method of iron and steel framing to build taller paid off: by 1891 he was a millionaire. Five years later he expanded the business to New York City, but he died in 1900 aged only 49. His son-in-law, Harry S Black, took over and one year later bought an awkward triangular block at the intersection of Broadway, 5th Avenue and 23rd Street near Madison Square Park as the future site of the Fuller Company's headquarters.

Burnham's Design

Black had hired the famous Chicago architect Daniel Hudson Burnham to design the headquarters even before the land was purchased. Faced with a site shaped like a flatiron, a mandate to build up to 20 storeys and a rushed schedule, Burnham was undeterred, excited to realize his first NYC building. Burnham's firm devised a skinny limestone- and terracotta-clad tower that filled most of the site and was capped by a cornice 1.2m (4ft) deep, 21 storeys above the pavement.

The elevations were articulated in a base–middle–top manner, akin to a classical column, while the repetitive middle sections on Broadway and 5th Avenue were broken up by subtle bay window protrusions.

Demolition

Demolition of the existing two- and three-storey buildings commenced in May 1901, but the Fuller Company hit a snag with the seven-storey Cumberland apartment building. It was the home of Colonel Winfield Scott Proskey, who, unlike the other tenants, refused to leave. He persisted even after the utilities were cut off, refusing a $5,000 offer to vacate. His story received national attention, but by mid-June lawyers had devised a way to evict Proskey, making way for the first Manhattan skyscraper north of 14th Street.

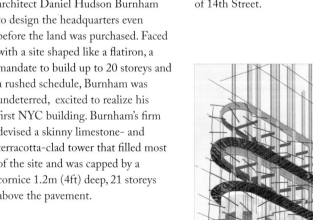

Curved steel beams were installed at the Flatiron Building's three corners.

BUILDING AND STRUCTURE

Construction

On 11 September 1901, a building permit was issued for the Fuller Building, which was already being called the Flatiron Building in the press. Workers then excavated for the concrete and granite foundations, which were only 10.6m (35ft) deep – the depth of bedrock below the triangular site. The riveted steel frame – manufactured in Pittsburgh, Pennsylvania, and transported to Manhattan via train, ferry and truck – rose from the foundations, but delays caused by a snowstorm and high demand for steel during the building boom meant slow progress at first.

Indiana limestone covering the base and terracotta tiles manufactured in Staten Island for the rest of the exterior followed, hung off the steel frame as was becoming the norm.

Reception

When completed at the beginning of October 1902, the 22-storey skyscraper got mixed reviews from critics, but these were balanced by widespread public affection. With its narrow prow facing Madison Square Park, people likened it to a ship sailing up the avenue, and artists captured the view in paintings and photographs. The Fuller Company changed the name of their building to the Flatiron shortly after completion, another indication that it belonged to the city and its inhabitants more than to the company that built it.

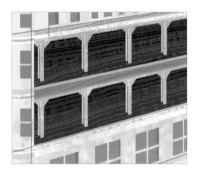

Engineer Corydon Purdy devised different types of bracing to stabilize the slender building in the wind.

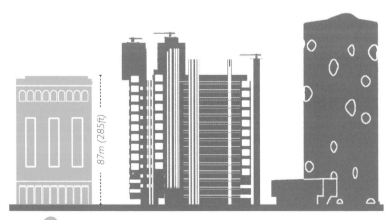

87m (285ft)

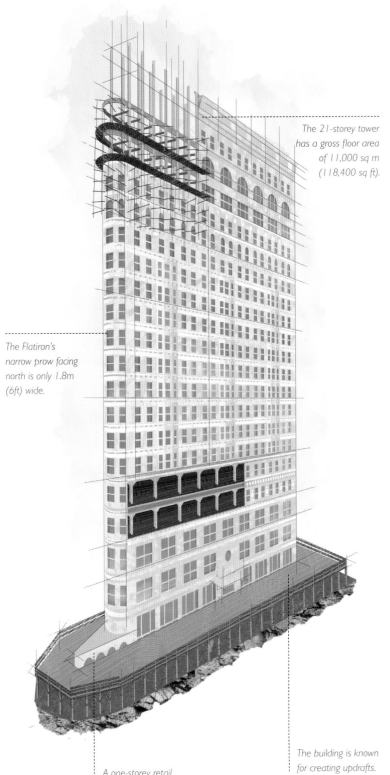

The 21-storey tower has a gross floor area of 11,000 sq m (118,400 sq ft).

The Flatiron's narrow prow facing north is only 1.8m (6ft) wide.

A one-storey retail 'prow' was added at the last minute at the suggestion of the client.

The building is known for creating updrafts.

WOOLWORTH BUILDING

Location: New York City, USA | **Completion:** 1913 | **Height:** 241m (792ft) | **Storeys:** 57 | **Primary Function:** Offices | **Owner/Developer:** F W Woolworth Company, Irving National Exchange Bank; Alchemy Properties, The Witkoff Group | **Architect:** Cass Gilbert **Structural Engineer:** Gunvald Aus Company | **Key Facts:** Tallest building in the world from 1913 until 1930. Dubbed the 'Cathedral of Commerce' by a reverend during its opening ceremony.

Frank Woolworth

Frank Winfield Woolworth founded his eponymous company in 1879, when he opened a five-cent store in Lancaster, Pennsylvania. Woolworth was very successful at selling goods at low prices and in 1910, when he commissioned architect Cass Gilbert to design Woolworth's headquarters, the company had nearly 300 outlets, including 20 in New York City alone. That number would double two years later, when shops that had operated as franchises were merged into the F W Woolworth Company. Woolworth's success is famously known through his ability to pay $13.5 million in cash for the building, half of it just for the land.

Cass Gilbert

Although Cass Gilbert had fewer than 20 buildings to his name in New York by 1910, his lavishly decorated Beaux-Arts designs had already made an impact on the cityscape. With a mandate to surpass the recently completed 213m (700ft) Metropolitan Life Tower near the Flatiron Building, Woolworth and Gilbert opted for the Flamboyant Gothic style. Gilbert believed this style would best achieve the vertical aspirations of building tall, at the same time as giving Woolworth the 'giant signboard' he desired for the site he had purchased overlooking City Hall Park in lower Manhattan.

Residential Conversion

Lower Manhattan's rapidly shifting demographics this century have meant that many buildings are being emptied of office space and converted to residences. The Woolworth Building is no exception, but it is exceptional: the top 30 floors are being turned into 33 privately owned apartments, including a seven-storey penthouse, where somebody will live within the crown that others see only from a distance.

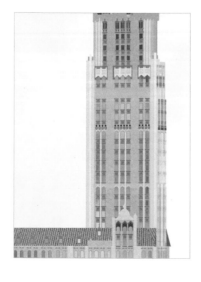

The slender tower rises above the larger base – 28 floors of offices are below and converted residences are above.

BUILDING AND STRUCTURE

Design

Gilbert followed Woolworth's suggestion to model the building on the Victoria Tower at London's Houses of Parliament (Woolworth was expanding into England at the time). The final design came together at the beginning of 1911: a 30-storey base with a U-shaped plan filling the width and depth of the site, and above it a slender, 23-storey tower capped by a copper-covered roof. The Gothic ornament gives the building an upward thrust as it extends proudly above the setback roofs. Gilbert's tiered massing was built three years before New York City mandated setbacks in its famous 1916 zoning resolution – the façade was reactionary, but the form was not.

Construction

Gilbert's team produced the construction documents for the tower in 90 days – a total of 1,550 drawings including those produced by the engineers. The Thompson–Starrett Company won the contract to build the tower and started by excavating to bedrock at depths of around 35m (115ft) for the concrete piers.

From the foundation rose 20,900 tonnes (20,500 tons) of steel columns and beams, connected with portal braces, diagonal bracing and other means of resisting wind forces. The terracotta façade was made in New Jersey and carried to the site at the rate of one truckload every 15 minutes. The large size of the skyscraper, the smallness of the site and the number of workers involved (2,000 at a time) pointed to the importance of logistics over sheer manual or machine labour.

Although the Gothic Revival terracotta exterior gives the tower a traditional appearance, a modern steel structure holds it up.

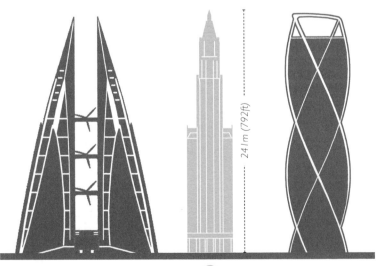

241m (792ft)

11

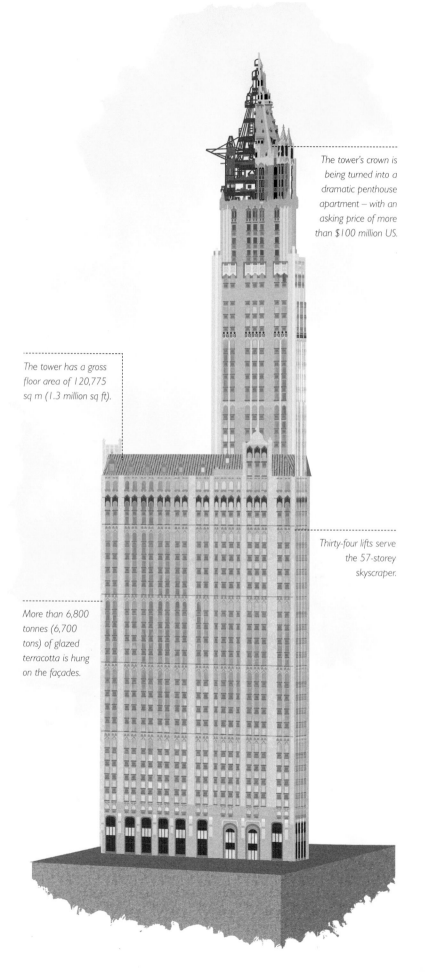

The tower's crown is being turned into a dramatic penthouse apartment – with an asking price of more than $100 million US.

The tower has a gross floor area of 120,775 sq m (1.3 million sq ft).

Thirty-four lifts serve the 57-storey skyscraper.

More than 6,800 tonnes (6,700 tons) of glazed terracotta is hung on the façades.

CHRYSLER BUILDING

LOCATION: New York City, USA | COMPLETION: 1930 | HEIGHT: 319m (1,046ft) | STOREYS: 77 | PRIMARY FUNCTION: Offices | OWNER/DEVELOPER: Tishman Speyer Properties, W P Chrysler Building Corporation | ARCHITECT: William van Alen | STRUCTURAL ENGINEER: Ralph Squire & Sons | KEY FACTS: The tallest building in the world for one year, from May 1930 until May 1931.

Historical Background

If all had gone right the first time, this iconic Manhattan tower would be known as the Reynolds Building. Developer and former State Senator William H Reynolds hired William Van Alen to design a 206m (808ft) tower at the corner of 42nd Street and Lexington Avenue, near Grand Central Terminal. But Reynolds ran out of money, so Walter P Chrysler bought the land and the project for $2 million US in October 1928.

Race to the Top

In the halcyon days between World War I and the Great Depression, Manhattan developers raced to build the tallest towers that money and engineering would allow. Two towers completed in 1930 grabbed the most attention: the Chrysler Building, and the Manhattan Company Building at 40 Wall Street, designed by H. Craig Severance. Although both would be eclipsed by the Empire State Building one year later, the Chrysler Building bested 40 Wall Street by more than 30.5m (100ft) – a sweet success for Van Alen, whose partnership with Severance had bitterly dissolved not long before.

The Spire

Van Alen's initial design featured its distinctive steel crown, but when Chrysler took over he directed him to raise the tower to 77 storeys – 282m (925ft). With Severance's tower hitting 283m 927ft) through the addition of a lantern and flagpole, something else was needed to nab the 'world's tallest' title. So Van Alen secretly designed a 56.4m (185ft) spire that was assembled inside a shaft in the middle of the building. The steel spire was lifted into place – 'like a butterfly from its cocoon', according to Van Alen – in only 90 minutes in November 1929, just after 40 Wall Street had topped off.

New York City's zoning code allowed for unlimited height when towers covered 25% of a given site, which created the distinctive setbacks at the base.

BUILDING AND STRUCTURE

Nirosta

The bulk of the Chrysler Building's curtain wall is a herringbone pattern of grey, white and black brick trimmed with white and black stone, but it is the metallic crown, spire and ornaments that give the skyscraper its memorable place on the skyline. The material these parts were covered in was called Nirosta, a chromium–nickel steel developed by Krupps for use in World War I; today it is known as stainless steel. It covers four gargoyles (modelled after a Chrysler radiator cap) at the corners of the 31st floor as well as eight eagles projecting 61 storeys above the street, and the crown. That crown is now the most famous top of any skyscraper, but its unprecedented design was derided in its time – one critic called it 'meaningless voluptuousness'.

The Crown

The crown is made up of five layers: the sheet metal exterior, wooden nailing strips, a thin layer of nailing concrete, the riveted steel frame, and sprayed gunite on the inside. While the complex angled pieces of structural steel were fabricated on the floor of a shipbuilding company and transported to the site, the metal cladding was produced in workshops on the 67th and 75th floors after measuring on site. Nirosta nails were used to avoid the corrosion that takes place when dissimilar metals touch – an invisible detail, but one that illustrates the care that accompanied the race to be tallest.

The triangular windows set into the steel crown glow at night, maintaining the tower's unmistakable presence into the late hours.

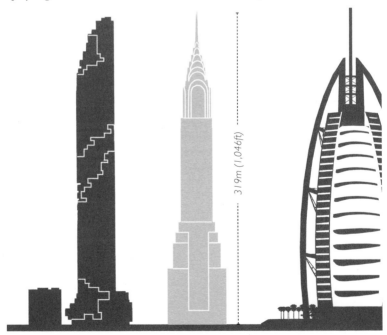

319m (1,046ft)

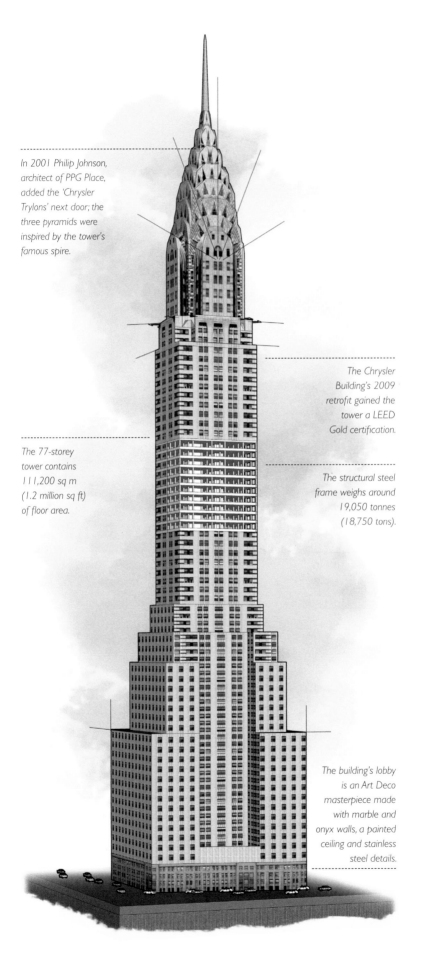

In 2001 Philip Johnson, architect of PPG Place, added the 'Chrysler Trylons' next door; the three pyramids were inspired by the tower's famous spire.

The Chrysler Building's 2009 retrofit gained the tower a LEED Gold certification.

The 77-storey tower contains 111,200 sq m (1.2 million sq ft) of floor area.

The structural steel frame weighs around 19,050 tonnes (18,750 tons).

The building's lobby is an Art Deco masterpiece made with marble and onyx walls, a painted ceiling and stainless steel details.

EMPIRE STATE BUILDING

LOCATION: New York City, USA | COMPLETION: 1931 | HEIGHT: 381m (1,250ft) | STOREYS: 102 | PRIMARY FUNCTION: Offices | OWNER/ DEVELOPER: Empire State Realty Trust, Qatar Investment Authority ARCHITECT: Shreve, Lamb & Harmon Associates | STRUCTURAL ENGINEER: H G Balcom & Associates | KEY FACTS: The tallest building in the world from 1931 to 1974.

An American Icon

The Empire State Building (ESB) is one of the most recognizable skyscrapers in the world and – according to a 2007 poll from the American Institute of Architects – the favourite building of Americans. Some of this appreciation stems from its once-enduring position as the world's tallest building, but most remarkable is the speed at which the tower was designed and built: 20 months from the signing of contracts in September 1929 to opening day on 1 May 1931.

Building Form

In 1929 John Jakob Raskob and his partners formed Empire State Inc., one year after their purchase of the site on which the Waldorf Astoria Hotel sat at 34th Street and 5th Avenue. The city was then in the midst of a building boom, when most structures took the form of 'wedding cakes' in response to the city's famous 1916 zoning resolution. Architect William Lamb went in a slightly different direction, filling the 0.8-hectare (2-acre) site to the fifth floor and then setting back to a tower rising another 80 floors. Smaller setbacks occurred in between, where lift shafts ended and gave way to rentable space. Economics and daylight dictated this almost pyramidal form: floor plates were to be no greater than 8.5m (28ft) from window to core.

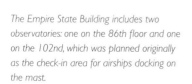

The Empire State Building includes two observatories: one on the 86th floor and one on the 102nd, which was planned originally as the check-in area for airships docking on the mast.

BUILDING AND STRUCTURE

Construction

Starrett Brothers and Eken oversaw construction, from demolition of the Waldorf Astoria Hotel – which started inauspiciously in October 1929, the month of the stock market crash – to completion. Thanks to round-the-clock work and a bedrock depth of only 10.7m (35ft), excavation work lasted only two months and wrapped up in March 1930. The steel structure rose at rates of up to 14 floors in 10 days, with concrete floor slabs and exterior façades close behind. Temporary tracks laid on each floor enabled the speedy delivery of materials, while Lamb's design of the curtain wall – simple limestone panels, aluminium spandrels and flush windows – sped erection.

Steel Structure

Engineer Homer G Balcom adopted the most common steel-framing technique at the time: riveting steel sections together. More than 51,700 tonnes (50,900 tons) of structural steel were placed in a six-month period, from the first columns set in April 1930 to the topping off of the tower at what would become the 86th-floor observation deck. Columns and beams were manufactured in Pittsburgh, shipped to New Jersey, ferried to Manhattan, trucked to the site, and then promptly installed – from manufacture to riveting, the process took only 80 hours.

The Mast

May 1930 saw the completion of the nearby Chrysler Building, its spire reaching to 319m (1,046ft), only 1.2m (4ft) short of the 85th floor of ESB, which was publicized to become the world's tallest tower. To ensure this title, Lamb designed a 61m (200ft) mast that took the skyscraper to 102 storeys and 381m (1,250ft).

The building is covered in 14,158 cu m (200,000 cu ft) of limestone.

This mast was justified as an anchor for the mooring of dirigibles, but only a couple of attempts were made – quickly thwarted by the updraughts the tower created. A 61m (200ft) television tower was placed atop the mast in 1953, but it is the lighting, first turned on in 1964, that helps to give the ESB its enduring presence on the New York skyline – at any time of day.

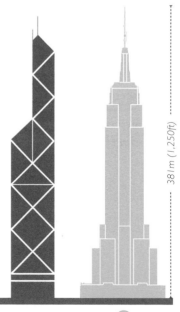

381 m (1,250ft)

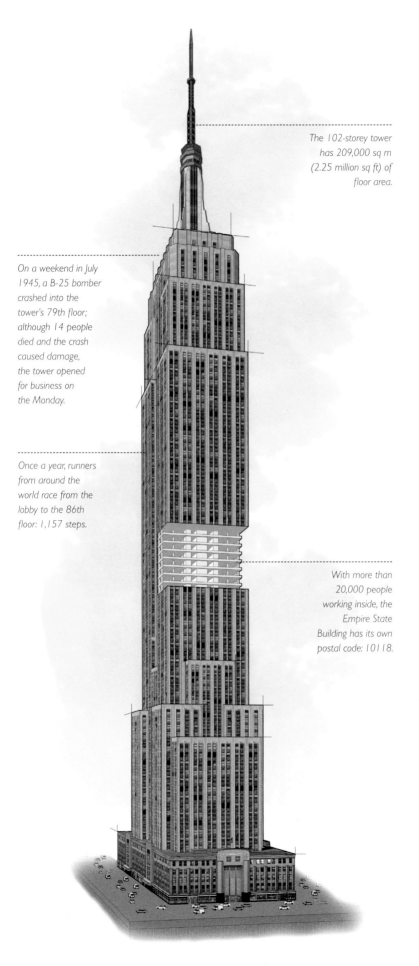

The 102-storey tower has 209,000 sq m (2.25 million sq ft) of floor area.

On a weekend in July 1945, a B-25 bomber crashed into the tower's 79th floor; although 14 people died and the crash caused damage, the tower opened for business on the Monday.

Once a year, runners from around the world race from the lobby to the 86th floor: 1,157 steps.

With more than 20,000 people working inside, the Empire State Building has its own postal code: 10118.

ONE WORLD TRADE CENTER

LOCATION: New York City, USA | **COMPLETION:** 2014 | **HEIGHT:** 541m (1,776ft) | **STOREYS:** 94 | **PRIMARY FUNCTION:** Offices | **OWNER/ DEVELOPER:** Port Authority of New York and New Jersey, The Durst Organization | **ARCHITECT:** Skidmore, Owings & Merrill (SOM) **STRUCTURAL ENGINEERS:** WSP Global, Schlaich Bergermann Partner (SBP) | **KEY FACTS:** The tallest building in the western hemisphere at the time of writing.

Site History

One World Trade Center (WTC) was born from the world's most horrific terrorist attack: the killing of more than 2,600 people in the Twin Towers when two hijacked planes flew into the buildings on 11 September 2001. Although not beloved like the Chrysler and Empire State buildings, the Twin Towers, designed by Minoru Yamasaki and completed in 1973, were nevertheless a symbol of New York City. Their destruction left a void in the skyline of Lower Manhattan – a void to be replaced with something taller.

The Master Plan

The backlash to a handful of uninspired rebuilding schemes unveiled in the middle of 2002 led to a design competition for the 6.5-hectare (16-acre) site. The process received enormous attention, and in February 2003 Daniel Libeskind's 'Memory Foundations' scheme was named the winner. Four towers arrayed around the footprints of the Twin Towers increased in height towards 'Freedom Tower', whose asymmetrical spire referenced the Statue of Liberty and which reached the symbolic height of 1,776ft (541m), commemorating the year of the Declaration of Independence.

Tower Design

David Childs of SOM was brought in to design the tower and when a groundbreaking ceremony was held in April 2006 for what would become the less patriotic-sounding One WTC, the only resemblance to Libeskind's winning design was the tower's height. Childs took the 280,000 sq m (3 million sq ft) project in a classically modern direction: the square plan, tapered section and rotated top add up to a tower that alludes to the Washington Monument in Washington, DC (completed 1884).

The perimeter steel framing wraps around the vertical and sloped surfaces to form what is in essence a tube system.

BUILDING AND STRUCTURE

Safety

Ahmad Rahimian and his associates at WSP designed One WTC as a hybrid structure made up of a concrete core with walls as thick as 1.37m (4½ft) and a perimeter framing system of high-strength structural steel (40,800 tonnes/40,150 tons of it); this system adds a level of redundancy to the structure. Furthermore, the core includes extrawide evacuation stairs; an additional layer of concrete walls 60cm (2ft) thick protects the lobby from car bombs; and outriggers at the mechanical floors near the roof give the tower added lateral stability.

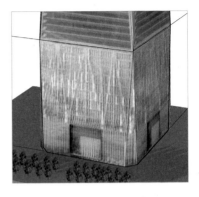

The tower's cubic concrete base is covered in more than 2,000 pieces of prismatic glass.

Construction

Obstacles abounded at the WTC site, but none more pressing than the tracks of the Port Authority Trans-Hudson (PATH) commuter trains, which crossed the tower's footprint and remained in operation during construction. The underground structure of the tower, which passes through four subterranean levels, had to snake its way over and between the tracks in order to reach bedrock at depths of 21m (70ft). Above ground, the steel exterior walls rose about ten floors ahead of the concrete core and supported shipping containers with lockers, restrooms and even a sandwich shop for the benefit of construction workers.

The Spire

Atop the building is a 134.4m (441ft) spire that sits inside three circular communication platforms and rises to 541m (1,776ft) from another symbolic height: the 417m (1,368ft)

roofline matches the height of the taller of the Twin Towers. Childs, working with SBP, designed the spire to be wrapped in a fibreglass radome, but value engineering in 2010 led to the wrapper's removal. Though the finished product is utilitarian rather than artistic, the Council on Tall Buildings and Urban Habitat (CTBUH) recognized the spire as part of the tower's 'architectural height', making it the tallest building in the western hemisphere.

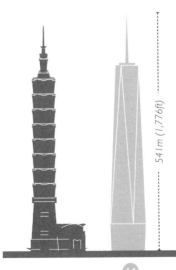

541m (1,776ft)

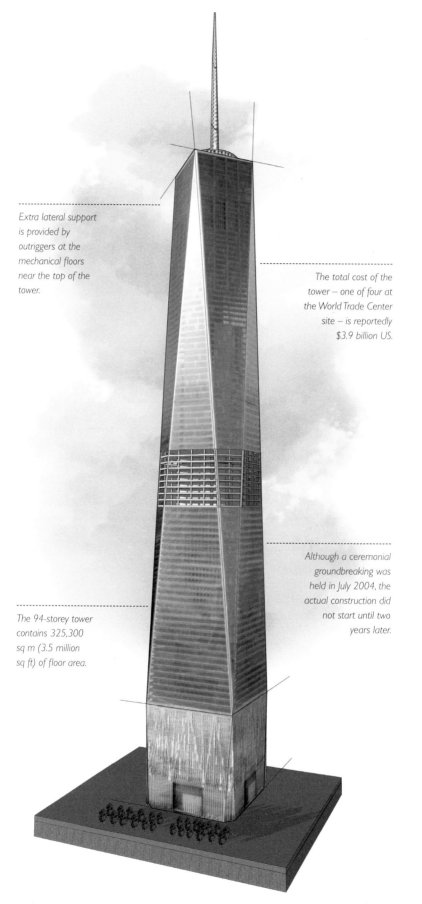

Extra lateral support is provided by outriggers at the mechanical floors near the top of the tower.

The total cost of the tower – one of four at the World Trade Center site – is reportedly $3.9 billion US.

Although a ceremonial groundbreaking was held in July 2004, the actual construction did not start until two years later.

The 94-storey tower contains 325,300 sq m (3.5 million sq ft) of floor area.

TORRE COSTANERA

Location: Santiago, Chile | **Completion:** 2014 | **Height:** 300m (984ft)
Storeys: 62 | **Primary Function:** Offices | **Owner/Developer:**
Cencosud | **Architect:** Pelli Clarke Pelli Architects; Alemparte Barreda y
Asociados | **Structural Engineer:** René Lagos y Asociados
Key Facts: The first supertall in South America; also the tallest
observatory in South America.

A Bold Statement

At more than 100m (330ft) taller
than the next tallest building in
Santiago, the capital of Chile, the
Torre Costanera – popularly known
as the Gran Torre Santiago – makes
a strong statement across the city's
skyline, particularly when glimpsed
against the Andean backdrop.
The tower anchors the ongoing
Costanera Center development
near the Mapocho River, in the
financial district referred to by
many as 'Sanhattan'.

Costanera Center

Developed by Cencosud, the retail
company headed by German-Chilean
entrepreneur Horst Paulmann,
Costanera Center consists of the
largest shopping mall in South
America, which opened in 2012,
and four proposed towers with office,
hotel and medical facilities; to date,
only Torre 2 – the tallest at 300m
(984ft) – has been built, at the site's

northwest corner. Canadian company
Watt International designed the
mall, while Argentina-born New
York architect César Pelli designed
the tower. Construction on the tower
commenced in 2006, but the
economic crisis of 2009 put the
project on hold for 10 months; that
and other delays ensured that the
tower's construction was not wrapped
up until well after Chile's bicentennial
in 2010.

*Floor-to-floor heights are tall: 6m (19.5ft)
for floors one to ten, and 4.1m (13½ft) for
floors 11 and above.*

BUILDING AND STRUCTURE

Building Form

The tower is basically an extruded square plan with a few variations that make it more than a simple box. First, each side of the square is bowed and bent slightly in the middle so as to reflect its surroundings at different angles. Second, the glass walls on the four sides stop short of the corners, which are recessed and have their own glass walls set at 45 degrees to the main ones. And third, the floor plan shrinks as the tower rises to give the skyscraper its tapered form; in turn, the four elevations taper in profile as the recessed corners grow in prominence. These variations give the impression that the tower is made up of four independent faces that do not meet, accentuated by the latticed crown that extends roughly 35m (115ft) past the 62nd-floor observation deck.

Double-deck elevators serve a sky lobby on the 36th floor and 'Sky Costanera' observatory on floors 61 and 62.

Structure

Reinforced concrete is the main structural material used for this first South American supertall. More than 72,000 cu m (2.5 million cu ft) of the material makes up the tower's core and its 16 columns (four per side) that reduce in size as the tower rises.

Floors of concrete and metal decking rest on steel beams, while more steel is used at the top of the building to frame the glass lattice. The whole, including five subterranean levels, is supported by an 18,000-tonne (17,700-ton) reinforced concrete mat foundation 3m (10ft) thick and 50m (164ft) square.

With Chile being extremely prone to earthquakes, lateral forces are always an integral consideration in the structural design. In winds as high as 122km/h (76mph) the tower moves only 13¾in (35cm) at the top. Although not topped out at the time, the tower's concrete structure was put to the test when an 8.8-magnitude quake hit central Chile in February 2010. It was one of the strongest earthquakes ever recorded by humans but the structure survived intact – a good omen for a building of such unprecedented height in the region.

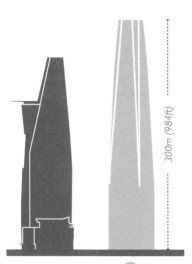

300m (984ft)

Mechanical floors are located on floors 7 and 51 and on the roof.

The 62-storey tower has 110,000 sq m (1.2 million sq ft) of floor area.

Glass was supplied from a company in China, and problems with the colour of the glass reportedly delayed the project by more than a year.

An on-site concrete plant produced 360 cu m (12,700 cu ft) of concrete every day during construction.

TORRE AGBAR

LOCATION: Barcelona, Spain | COMPLETION: 2004 | HEIGHT: 144m (472ft) | STOREYS: 35 | PRIMARY FUNCTION: Offices | OWNER/ DEVELOPER: Layetana Real Estate | ARCHITECT: Ateliers Jean Nouvel, b720 Fermín Vázquez Arquitectos | STRUCTURAL ENGINEER: Robert Brufau i Associats; Brufau, Obiol, Moya i Associats | KEY FACTS: Third-tallest building in Barcelona, where all are shorter than the tallest point on Antoni Gaudí's Sagrada Família church (under construction since 1882).

A Rising Singularity

Architect Jean Nouvel's describes the headquarters of Sociedad General de Aguas de Barcelona (Agbar) on his website as 'not a tower [nor] a skyscraper'. Instead, the building is a 'rising singularity… a fluid mass that bursts through the ground like a geyser'. Though one could argue easily that the elliptical building is in fact a tower, this metaphor is apt, given that Agbar is the company responsible for supplying Barcelona with clean water. Even though Agbar moved out in 2015 and sold the building in early 2017, the tower's form, structure and colour express the idea that the tower is something special.

Form

Torre Agbar was completed in the same year as 30 St Mary Axe (page 84), a fact that made their strikingly similar forms a constant point of comparison; it is hard to avoid comparing them more than a dozen years later.

While the tower designed by Norman Foster for the City of London is circular with a central core, Nouvel's design is elliptical with an egg-shaped core set off-centre. The latter's shapes relate to Torre Agbar's location in the new Plaça de les Glòries Catalanes commercial district, adjacent to Avinguda Diagonal, and they give the plan an axis that subtly points northwest towards the mountains.

Clear glass covers the dome over the upper floors of the tower, where executives are located.

BUILDING AND STRUCTURE

Structure

Another difference between the British and Spanish towers is found in their structural expressions: 30 St Mary Axe proudly displays its steel diagrid, while Torre Agbar cloaks its 50cm (20in) deep concrete shell behind a façade of glass and aluminium. The steel frame enables Foster's tower to bow out before it tapers towards its tip, but Nouvel's concrete ellipse rises straight up from its four-storey-deep basement to the 25th floor, after which a steel-framed dome tapers to a point.

Structurally, the concrete exterior works with the concrete core – nested walls linked by castellated steel beams (for running services) and concrete floors on lightweight decking. The concrete core and perimeter walls were poured with a patented climbing form system that used one-storey mould panels, prefabricated steel cages for reinforcing and a pump located in the centrer of the core. Above level 25, the prestressed concrete floors are cantilevered from the core, which itself is capped off elegantly, like a missile housed in a glass-roofed silo.

Colour

The most conspicuous difference between the two bullet-shaped towers is Nouvel's unabashed use of colour. The concrete perimeter – punctured by more than 4,400 small windows in various configurations – is covered in two layers: a sandwich of insulation, air space and corrugated aluminium sheets; and glass louvres a few feet in front, hung on vertical aluminium rails.

Photovoltaic panels are incorporated into some parts of the façade, while sensors activate louvres in front of the windows.

The corrugated aluminium is the canvas for colour: primarily red at the base, 'dissipating' to white and blue near the top, where Nouvel wanted the glass dome to make the building blur like a mirage into the sky. This effect is aided by the glass louvres, which cut down on direct sunlight during the day, but whose surface textures give the exterior its gauzy appearance. At night, though, when LEDs illuminate the façade's cavity, the tower is a riot of colour, a modern take on the work of the city's most famous architect, Antoni Gaudí.

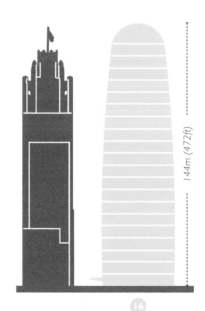

144m (472ft)

16

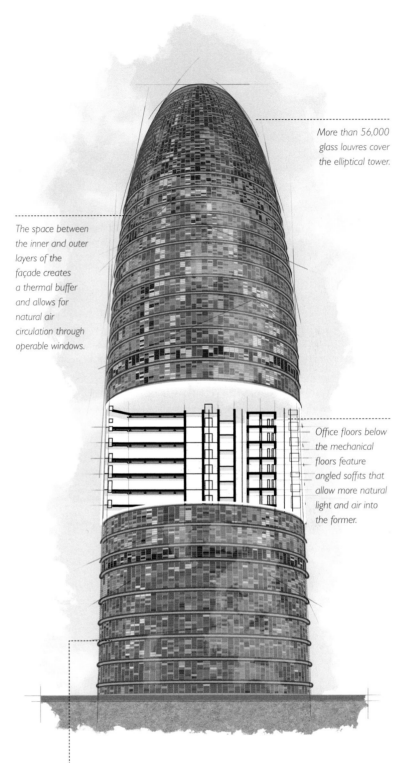

More than 56,000 glass louvres cover the elliptical tower.

The space between the inner and outer layers of the façade creates a thermal buffer and allows for natural air circulation through operable windows.

Office floors below the mechanical floors feature angled soffits that allow more natural light and air into the former.

The 35-storey tower has a gross floor area of 47,500 sq m (511,286 sq ft).

TORRE CEPSA

LOCATION: Madrid, Spain | **COMPLETION:** 2008 | **HEIGHT:** 248m (815ft)
STOREYS: 49 | **PRIMARY FUNCTION:** Offices | **OWNER/DEVELOPER:**
Pontegadea Inmobiliaria, Bankia, Khadem al-Qubaisi; Repsol YPF
ARCHITECTS: Foster + Partners, Gonzalo Martínez-Pita Copello
STRUCTURAL ENGINEER: Halvorson and Partners | **KEY FACTS:**
The second-tallest tower in Spain – shorter than the adjacent Torre
de Cristal (2008) by less than 1m (3ft).

Four Towers

For decades the Ciudad Sportiva
(Sport City) sat on the northern
outskirts of Madrid with training
facilities for the prestigious Real
Madrid soccer club. As the city grew
around it, the large area was eyed for
commercial development, and early
this century it became the site of the
Cuatro Torres Business Area. Four
developers were responsible for one of
each of the four towers, and the most
distinctive of these is the tower
Norman Foster's firm designed for
Repsol YPF.

Changing Hands

The tower was originally planned as
the headquarters of oil and gas
company Repsol, but one year before
its 2008 completion it was sold to
Caja Madrid, Spain's oldest savings
bank. It consolidated with a number
of other banks in 2010, so the tower
was known as Torre Bankia until
Cepsa, another oil and gas company,
signed an eight-year lease in 2013.
The tower sold yet again in 2016
(to the real estate company of
Amancio Ortega, Europe's richest
person), but it retains the name of its
main tenant.

Flexibility

The ease with which the tower can
serve different owners and occupants
stems in part from the relatively
unobstructed floor plates on every
office floor. These are enabled by the
placement of the cores – with their
lifts, stairs and bathrooms – at the
east and west ends of the rectangular
plan. In effect, the cores are like a pair
of giant legs holding the office floors
between them. At the top, the 'legs'
are connected to form an arch; the
opening beneath this was originally
designed to accommodate wind
turbines, if the owner wished to
install them.

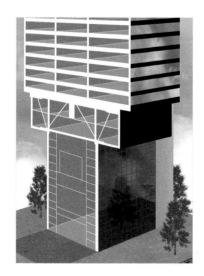

*The atrium takes up the first 22m (72ft)
of the structure above ground.*

BUILDING AND STRUCTURE

Structure

Although now free of turbines, the opening minimizes the lateral wind forces acting upon the tower. Vertical forces are taken care of by the beefy reinforced concrete cores that extend from the concrete mat five storeys below ground (where underground parking is found) to the very top of the building. The office floors are separated into three sections (11, 12 and 11 storeys each) that are framed in steel and supported by two-storey-tall Vierendeel trusses at intermediate mechanical levels. These trusses transfer the loads from the office floors to the cores at their sides; further, they work with the cores to stiffen the tower through the creation of a 'megaframe'. Halvorson and Partners designed the structure with redundancy, so the larger system will remain stable even if any truss members are damaged locally.

Façade

The structural logic and the flexibility that this affords is accentuated by the cladding: stainless steel panels on the cores and at the top with its undulating underside; triple-glazed curtain walls with solar protective coatings on the cantilevered office floors; and clear-glass walls at the 22m (72ft) tall lobby, where a glass-walled auditorium 'floats' within the space. Dark recessed louvres at the mechanical floors help to express the three sections of the office floors. At night, coloured lights draw attention to the cores and the glass-walled lifts that sit behind glass façades, bookended by the concrete stairs.

The space above the offices is available for wind turbines to be installed, should the owner choose to do so. Turbines would contribute significantly to the building's power supply.

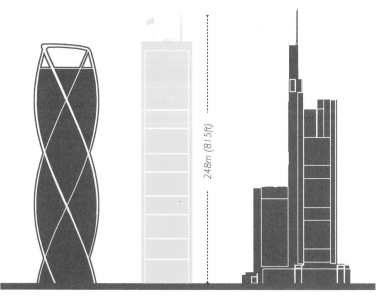

248m (815ft)

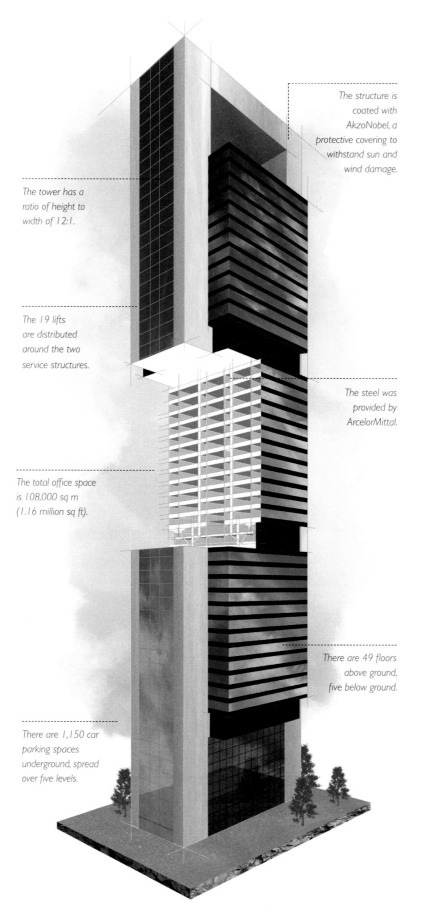

The structure is coated with AkzoNobel, a protective covering to withstand sun and wind damage.

The tower has a ratio of height to width of 12:1.

The 19 lifts are distributed around the two service structures.

The steel was provided by ArcelorMittal.

The total office space is 108,000 sq m (1.16 million sq ft).

There are 49 floors above ground, five below ground.

There are 1,150 car parking spaces underground, spread over five levels.

CENTRE POINT

LOCATION: London, England | COMPLETION: 1966 | HEIGHT: 117m (385ft) | STOREYS: 34 | PRIMARY FUNCTION: Residential (originally offices) | OWNER/DEVELOPER: Harry Hyams, Almacantar | ARCHITECT: Richard Seifert & Partners, Rick Mather Architects, and Conran & Partners | STRUCTURAL ENGINEER: Pell Frischmann | KEY FACTS: The world's tallest precast concrete office building when completed. A protected landmark since 1995.

Site History – and Future

As its name implies, Centre Point is centrally located in London, at St Giles Circus in Camden – the intersection of New Oxford Street, Charing Cross Road and Tottenham Court Road. The project as built consisted of a 34-storey office tower, 36 apartments on a neighbouring site, and an enclosed bridge connecting the two over a street (which has since been closed to enable the creation of a new square). The project sits adjacent to the Tottenham Court Road tube station, which will be a stop on the long-planned and much-anticipated Elizabeth Line.

Public–Private Partnership

In the mid-1950s the London County Council determined it needed a bus turnaround at St Giles Circus, so it worked with a private developer – Harry Hyams and his Oldham Estates – to acquire parcels of land and help finance the project. The partnership enabled Hyams to build twice as much floor area as would otherwise have been allowed. To pull it off, he had his architect push through an early plan for approval even before all of the sites were acquired. This controversial tactic was exacerbated by the fact that the bus turnaround was eventually dropped (even so, the car-orientated plan remained) and Hyams kept the tower empty for nearly a decade after its completion as he waited for rents in the area to rise to the desired level.

Below the flat top of the roof is the name of the building spelt out in storey-high letters.

BUILDING AND STRUCTURE

With the cores located at the ends of the narrow plan, the centre of the building is fairly open and allows for large residential units.

Richard Seifert & Partners

In 1995, decades after the initial controversies, Centre Point earned a Grade II listing, which protects it from being demolished or altered without special permission. This stemmed in part from a resurgence in the appeal of Brutalist architecture and a reappraisal of Richard Seifert's oeuvre; a primarily commercial architect, he transformed much of London in the 1960s and 1970s, often in partnership with Hyams. The architect in Seifert's office responsible for Centre Point was George Marsh, who turned Seifert's initial glassy design into a concrete masterpiece.

Concrete Façade

The tower's load-bearing concrete structure, whose narrow plan with convex sides resembles the 1958 Pirelli Building in Milan, is covered by a grid of precast concrete panels. The panels are upside-down T-shapes with the vertical chord flat and the horizontal pieces angled back towards the deep-set windows. This repeated shape gives the tower's four elevations a faceted appearance and enables the used of corner windows at the four corners of the plan as well as in the inset notches at the short ends. The tower is propped upon six large concrete *pilotis* (load-bearing pillars) that are pinched in the middle to reiterate the form of the precast panels above.

Residential Renovation

Most of Seifert's London towers were offices (as was the norm in many cities in the middle of last century), but nowadays narrow plans like that of Centre Point are better suited to residences.

Developer Almacantar (which bought Centre Point in 2011) has converted the tower into 82 apartments but has maintained the building's landmark external appearance. Over 4,200 sq m (45,000 sq ft) of new restaurants will also be introduced to the scheme. In the retrofit plan by Rick Mather Architects (with Terence Conran's firm doing the residential interiors), the street cutting across the site will be removed in favour of a pedestrian square – overcoming another controversial aspect of this enduring 1960s project.

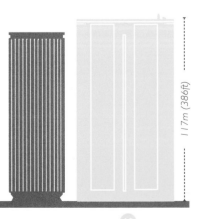

117m (386ft)

The 35-storey tower has 27,150 sq m (292,500 sq ft) of floor area.

The tower was one of the first buildings in England to be constructed with precast concrete panels.

The 82 new apartments in the converted office tower range in price from £3 million to £55 million.

LLOYD'S BUILDING

LOCATION: London, England | **COMPLETION:** 1986 | **HEIGHT:** 95m (312ft)
STOREYS: 14 | **PRIMARY FUNCTION:** Offices | **OWNER/DEVELOPER:**
Lloyd's of London, Ping An Insurance | **ARCHITECT:** Richard Rogers
Partnership | **STRUCTURAL ENGINEER:** Arup | **KEY FACTS:** The youngest
building to earn a Grade I listing, which it received in 2011. Lloyd's sold its
namesake building in 2005, and in 2013 it was sold to China's Ping An.

Historical Context

Lloyd's insurance company have been managing risk for businesses for more than 325 years. The market started in a London coffee shop, moved into the Royal Exchange, and then, in 1928, into its own building, which was expanded 30 years later. By 1977 Lloyd's was in need of modernization and additional space, so it invited a dozen architects to compete to design its new headquarters on Lime Street in the City, London's historic core. Richard Rogers, who had recently completed the celebrated Pompidou Centre in Paris with Renzo Piano, won with an overtly high-tech design that again placed services outside the façade in order to make office spaces more flexible.

The placement of the towers gives the symmetrical plan an asymmetrical appearance that is accentuated by the dense surroundings: the building is never glimpsed in its entirety, but rather as vertical slices of steel, concrete and glass. A façade from the 1928 building was retained at one corner of the site; this sort of strange juxtaposition of old and new was reiterated inside with the re-creation of an 18th-century dining room in the basement and the preserved Lutine Bell (a ship's bell from 1779, rung to commemorate events of national importance) in the Underwriting Room.

Design

The plan by Rogers and his team placed a rectangular footprint with central atrium in the middle of the irregular trapezoidal site, while six service towers (three for firefighting and stairs and three for washrooms, lifts and risers) were situated in the spaces between the rectangle and the property line.

The blue cranes atop the service towers were meant to be temporary, just for construction, but were eventually incorporated into the finished building.

BUILDING AND STRUCTURE

Structure

Rogers had worked with Arup engineer Peter Rice on the Pompidou Centre, and their first idea was to use a similar articulated steel structure for Lloyd's. But the London Fire Brigade pushed for concrete over steel and the pair relented, aiming to make 'the best concrete building in Britain'. Outside the exterior walls and on the edges of the full-height atrium are reinforced concrete columns on a 10.7m (35ft) grid. Precast concrete brackets and 'yokes' support the prestressed inverted-U beams that transfer loads from the floors to the columns. Some steel is used: tubes filled with concrete for diagonal bracing on the façades, and tubular steel at the atrium roof, whose vaulted form resembles Joseph Paxton's Crystal Palace from 1851.

The building uses 30,000 sq m (323,000 sq ft) of stainless steel cladding and 12,000 sq m (129,000 sq ft) of glass.

Construction

Foundation work commenced in June 1981 and, with 66 months allotted for construction, Lloyd's moved their underwriters and other employees into the building at Easter, 1986. Some prefabricated components sped up construction, notably the metal staircases and the washroom modules attached to the service towers. Although Rogers detailed raised flooring and other features for infrastructural flexibility, additional requirements for IT and accompanied power, determined in the course of construction, led to new plant space being installed atop the service towers, making them top-heavy and less slim than their original profiles.

Impact

Although the office boom that followed the construction of the Lloyd's Building shifted east from the City to the Docklands area, it returned in the new century as numerous tall towers crowded around Rogers' high-tech statement. The architect had given Lloyd's a building that pushed the market into the 21st century – and he did the same for the City of London, which has not looked the same since.

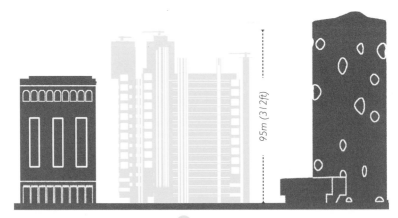

95m (312ft)

The 14-storey
building has
55,000 sq m
(592,000 sq ft)
of floor area.

The placement of
stairs, washrooms
and other services at
the building's
perimeter is a high-
tech variation on
Louis Kahn's idea
of 'served and
servant' spaces.

The building steps
from seven storeys on
the south to fourteen
on the north, bringing
natural light to the
central atrium.

83

The structure contains
33,510 cu m
(1.18 million cu ft)
of concrete.

30
ST MARY AXE

LOCATION: London, England | COMPLETION: 2004 | HEIGHT: 180m (590ft) | STOREYS: 40 | PRIMARY FUNCTION: Offices | OWNER/ DEVELOPER: Evans Randall, IVG; Swiss Re | ARCHITECT: Foster + Partners | STRUCTURAL ENGINEER: Arup | KEY FACTS: The world's first full diagrid office tower. Winner of 2004 RIBA Stirling Prize. Popularly known as 'The Gherkin'.

Site History

London's beloved contemporary icon grew on the site of tragedy: the 1992 bombing by the Irish Republican Army (IRA) of the historic Baltic Exchange building (completed 1903). Damaged beyond repair, the building was taken down, opening up a void in the city's financial district. Trafalgar House purchased the site but then, following an unsuccessful attempt to erect the supertall Millennium Tower, sold it to Swiss Reinsurance (Swiss Re) in 1998 for their corporate headquarters. Swiss Re hired architect Norman Foster, who wanted to maintain some of the breathing room born from the destruction.

Building Form

Although known as 'The Gherkin' (pickled cucumber) by the public, the tower's shape is actually more similar to the shape of a bullet. The circular 40-storey building bulges out from its base up to the sixth floor, increases in diameter slightly up to the twenty-firstst floor and then tapers elegantly to its apex. This unprecedented form arose from aerodynamics and the desire for a plaza. Squared-off towers, Foster contends, create downdraughts and wind vortices, but circular forms minimize wind deflections, thereby turning the plaza into a pleasant place to be, not one made unusable by gales of wind.

Behind the dark panes of glass are spiralling atriums that allow natural air into the office floors.

BUILDING AND STRUCTURE

Structure

30 St Mary Axe, the building's less descriptive yet official name, is hardly the first circular tower, but it is the first one to be encircled in a diagrid, where a traditional column-and-beam exterior is eschewed in favour of diagonal members in diamond formations. This system uses about 20 per cent less steel than a typical frame, with the added benefit of addressing both vertical and lateral loads, thereby freeing the core from a structural role. A diagrid is neither standard nor cheap; this one is made of two-storey-tall tubular steel members connected to nodes that, given the building's form, are different at each height. Intermediate hoops keep the diagonal members from deflecting outwards, while radial beams tie the exterior frame to the steel-framed core.

Plan

The combination of a tapered, cylindrical form and a diagrid structure led to the integration of V-shaped cutouts that spiral up the building. These segment each floor into six 'fingers', although in some cases the notches were floored over to create more usable space. A restaurant, bar and membership-only club sit atop the tower, below the fully glazed geodesic dome.

Ventilation

The spiralling notches give the tower its distinctive external appearance, but they are also integral to the natural ventilation strategy Foster's team developed with Arup. Operable windows draw air into the atriums, while the building's form draws the air across the floor plates and out of the building; it was an idea Foster first executed with Commerzbank in Frankfurt (page 92) but carried out

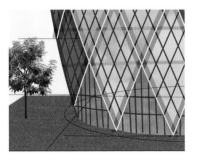

An arcade rings the base, like an extension of the plaza beneath the tower.

here on a smaller scale. Two layers of glass cover the offices: insulated glazing on the outside, and single-layer sliding glass walls inside; operable sunshades are located in the ventilated gap, while slots in the outer wall draw and exhaust air as part of the building's heating, ventilation and air conditioning (HVAC) system. These and other measures mean the building uses about half the energy of a conventionally air-conditioned office tower – another justification for its radical form.

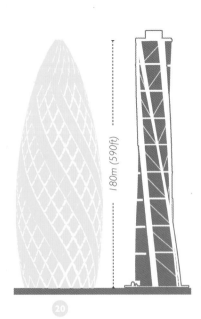

180m (590ft)

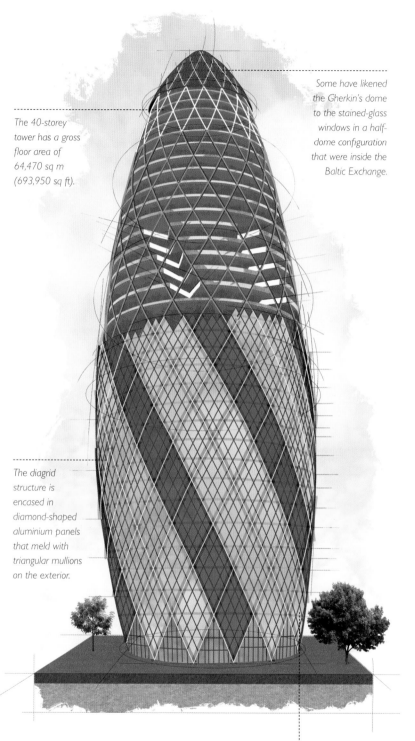

Some have likened the Gherkin's dome to the stained-glass windows in a half-dome configuration that were inside the Baltic Exchange.

The 40-storey tower has a gross floor area of 64,470 sq m (693,950 sq ft).

The diagrid structure is encased in diamond-shaped aluminium panels that meld with triangular mullions on the exterior.

The tower is covered with 24,000 sq m (258,333 sq ft) of glass in diamond-shaped configurations.

THE
SHARD

LOCATION: London, England | COMPLETION: 2013 | HEIGHT: 306m
(1,004ft) | STOREYS: 72 | PRIMARY FUNCTIONS: Residential, hotel, offices
OWNER/DEVELOPER: London Bridge Quarter, Sellar Property Group,
State of Qatar | ARCHITECTS: Renzo Piano Building Workshop, Adamson
Associates | STRUCTURAL ENGINEER: WSP Global | KEY FACTS:
The tallest tower in Western Europe at the time of writing.

The Site

The Shard is the descriptive and memorable name for the London Bridge Tower, the tallest component in the three-building London Bridge complex in the city's Southwark borough. The development takes its name from London Bridge Station, which stands next to The Shard and enables the tower to get by with only 48 parking spaces – just one amazing fact about a tower where 8,000 people live and work.

Mixed Uses

When developer Irvine Sellar proposed the city's tallest tower not long after the Millennium celebrations, Ken Livingstone was Mayor of London. He would go on to introduce a congestion charge (a levy to discourage vehicle use) for central London, but south of the Thames he wanted a large mixed-use project with strong connections to the rest of the city. Sellar and his architect, Renzo Piano, proposed a pyramidal tower stacked with three commercial floors, twenty-five floors of offices, restaurants on three floors, a seventeen-storey hotel, thirteen floors of apartments and a four-storey observatory. After a yearlong planning inquiry addressing the unprecedented height, the project received the go-ahead in November 2003.

The Shard's Shards

Although some sources describe The Shard as a 95-storey skyscraper, in reality it has 72 occupiable floors, an exterior stair reaching to the 87th floor, and cantilevered glass walls extending the rest of the way; the last are the shards that give the tower its name. These double-walled glass planes start just above the canopies at the base of the building and overlap each other to hint at the irregular six- and seven-sided floor plans. At the top The Shard's shards are angled off to dissolve into the sky. If the glass shards continued they would meet at one point 360m (1,181ft) high, more than 50m (165ft) above the tower's actual tip.

Any excess heat generated in the building is exhausted via 15 cooling radiator floors behind the open spire.

BUILDING AND STRUCTURE

Structure

With offices occupying the larger floor plates at the base of The Shard, and with hotels and apartments above, the engineers at WSP needed to devise a composite structure: steel framing for the first 40 floors, a post-tensioned concrete frame up to level 72, and a then steel spire on top. Respectively, columns are spaced at 6m (20ft), 3m (10ft) and 1.5m (5ft). The concrete midsection played an integral role functionally and structurally: the shallower floor-to-floor heights of the hotel and residences enabled two extra floors to be inserted, and the material provided damping to control the building's lateral sway and eliminate the need for a tuned mass damper in the upper floors.

Construction

When it came time to build the supertall tower, the most innovative features of its construction were utilized in the steel sections. The base was executed using top-down construction, whereby the first 23

floors of the 72-storey concrete core were poured before the 20m (66ft) deep basement was fully excavated. This is reported to have sped up construction by four months, the difference between enclosing the building fully before the 2012 Summer Olympics or after. Up top, the spire's 460 pieces of steel were prefabricated and preassembled off-site, another means of speeding up construction and minimizing the amount of time needed for erecting at such heights.

Eight sloping glass 'shards' provide fragmented reflections of the tower's surroundings.

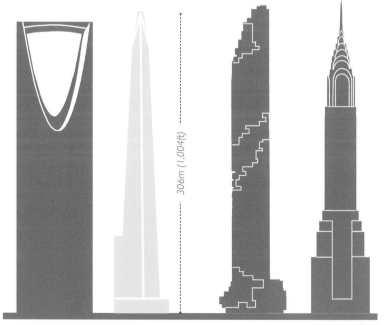

306m (1,004ft)

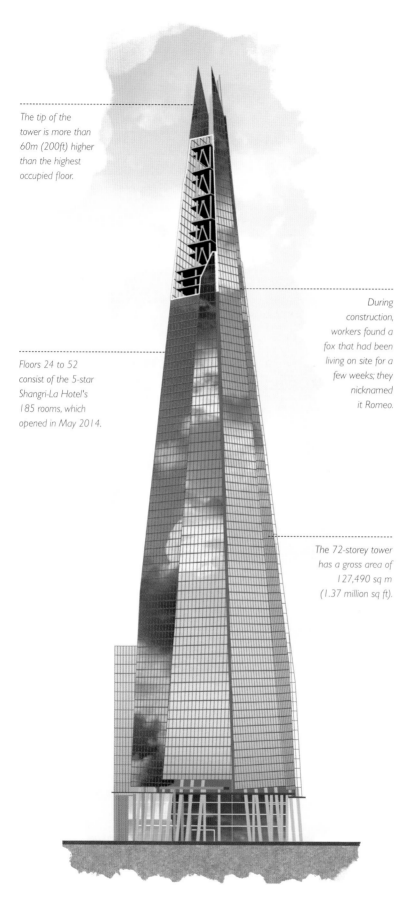

The tip of the tower is more than 60m (200ft) higher than the highest occupied floor.

During construction, workers found a fox that had been living on site for a few weeks; they nicknamed it Romeo.

Floors 24 to 52 consist of the 5-star Shangri-La Hotel's 185 rooms, which opened in May 2014.

The 72-storey tower has a gross area of 127,490 sq m (1.37 million sq ft).

COMMERZBANK TOWER

LOCATION: Frankfurt am Main, Germany | COMPLETION: 1997
HEIGHT: 259m (850ft) | STOREYS: 56 | PRIMARY FUNCTION: Offices
OWNER/DEVELOPER: Commerzbank | ARCHITECT: Foster + Partners
STRUCTURAL ENGINEER: Arup; Krebs + Kiefer | KEY FACTS: Considered
the first ecological, or environmentally friendly, high-rise in the world.
Europe's tallest building from 1997 to 2005.

Design Overview

Given Germany's leadership in building sustainably, it's no wonder that the country is home to the world's first ecological tower. Located next to Commerzbank's existing facilities in Frankfurt's dense banking district, the 1991 competition-winning design by Norman Foster provides daylight and fresh air to all of the bank's employees; this is achieved by a double-skin façade and sky gardens arranged around a full-height central atrium.

Cores

Since the development of skyscraper typology in the late 19th century, the preferred location of the core – where lifts, fire stairs, risers and other vertical services are located – has been in the middle of the plan, leaving the perimeter for occupiable space. At Commerzbank Tower the centre is given over to a void that enables natural ventilation, so in turn the cores with their lifts, fire stairs and washrooms are dispersed to the three corners of the triangular plan.

Structure

With the core shifted from the centre to the corners, the main vertical structure was moved outboard as well. Arup engineers placed a pair of steel-composite 'megacolumns' at each corner, splayed out to follow the triangular plan. This leaves the rounded tips of the corners free, allowing for glass walls that provide light to the elevator lobbies and provide conference rooms with dramatic views over the city. These megacolumns are linked together through eight-storey Vierendeel trusses that meet at the atrium's corner columns and support eight floors of clear-span offices.

The plants in the nine sky gardens spiralling up the triangular tower come from different regions depending on their exposure: North American, Asian and Mediterranean.

BUILDING AND STRUCTURE

Sky Gardens

On each side of the building the eight floors of offices alternate with four-storey-high sky gardens. Nine gardens spiral around the building, such that two of the three wings on each floor serve as office space, while the third is given over to a sky garden. These generous spaces bring in natural light, create smaller 'communities' within the tower, and give employees facing the central atrium views of a garden – and the city beyond. The gardens are accessible year-round for employees to take a break or hold informal meetings.

Natural Ventilation

The sky gardens bring trees and plants inside the 108,000 sq m (1.16 million sq ft) tower, but they also work with the triangular atrium to introduce fresh air and exhaust stale air. Outside air is brought in through vents at the gardens and pulled up naturally via the stack effect of the atrium, which is segmented by glass bulkheads for fire protection. At the office wings, the exterior glass walls are made of two glazed layers – a closed outer layer with controlled, dedicated intakes, and an inner layer with operable windows. The windows on the atrium are also operable. This passive ventilation is supplemented by a mechanical system, but the former prevails for 80 per cent of the year.

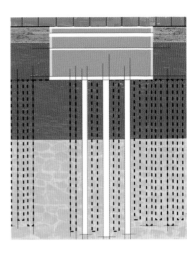

The tower's megacolumns and other superstructure components are distributed across a deep mat to over 100 large cast-in-place bored piles.

The Spire

Commerzbank Tower was the tallest tower in Europe when it was completed in 1997, an honour it held on to until 2005. Its height is made more dramatic by its asymmetrical top, where one corner core extends past the others and pushes its antenna to 300m (984ft), like a beacon of sustainability.

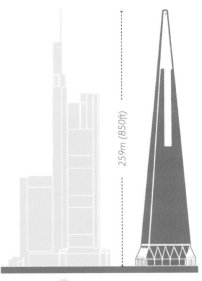

259m (850ft)

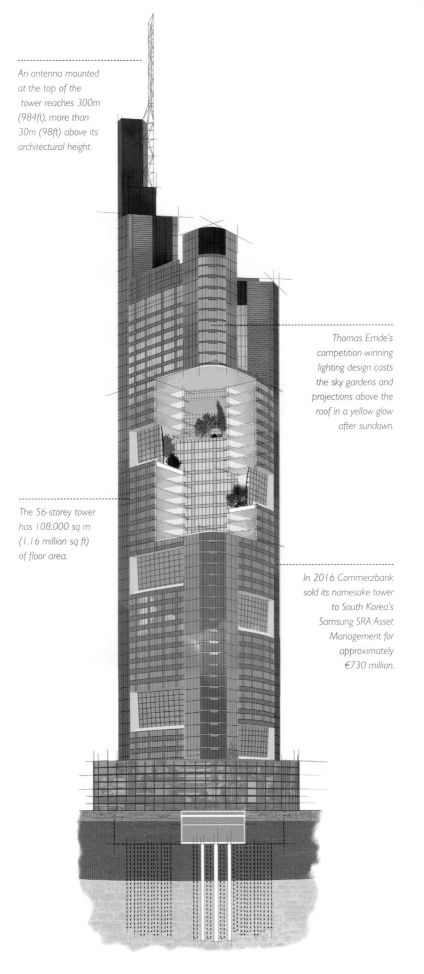

An antenna mounted at the top of the tower reaches 300m (984ft), more than 30m (98ft) above its architectural height.

Thomas Emde's competition-winning lighting design casts the sky gardens and projections above the roof in a yellow glow after sundown.

The 56-storey tower has 108,000 sq m (1.16 million sq ft) of floor area.

In 2016 Commerzbank sold its namesake tower to South Korea's Samsung SRA Asset Management for approximately €730 million.

PIRELLI TOWER

LOCATION: Milan, Italy | COMPLETION: 1958 | HEIGHT: 127m (417ft)
STOREYS: 32 | PRIMARY FUNCTION: Offices | OWNER/DEVELOPER:
Pirelli & C. SpA, Regional Government of Lombardy | ARCHITECT:
Gio Ponti | STRUCTURAL ENGINEERS: Pier Luigi Nervi, Arturo Danusso
KEY FACTS: The world's tallest reinforced-concrete building when completed.

Location

Most visitors to Milan probably happen upon the Pirelli Building when walking out of the main railway station north of the city centre. A modern office tower in such a predominantly low-rise context may seem jarring, but it was the logical outcome of a number of forces: the station's relocation near Pirelli's 19th-century factory in the 1930s; the destruction of the tyre company's plant during World War II; and Milan's 1953 city plan, which designated an area near the station for large office buildings.

Gio Ponti

For Alberto and Piero Pirelli, sons of company founder Giovanni Battista Pirelli, the first task was getting the city to approve the tower's height and its setback from the street – two guarantees of a modern building. Next they hired architect Gio Ponti, the well-known founder of *Domus* magazine, who designed everything from furniture to buildings. The brothers tasked him with designing a monument that would be dignified in its proportions, materials and details.

Pier Luigi Nervi

An integral member of Ponti's team was the structural engineer Pier Luigi Nervi, known for long-span structures in ferroconcrete, a system he developed using flexible steel mesh for reinforcement. The Pirelli Tower was Nervi's first tall building, but it would not be his last. Furthermore, the design that Ponti and Nervi developed together (with engineer Arturo Danusso) would influence other mid-century towers, most overtly the PanAm (now MetLife) Building in New York and Centre Point in London (page 76).

Behind the glass walls at the top of the tower, below the 'floating roof', is an observatory with panoramic views of Milan.

BUILDING AND STRUCTURE

The Plan

Functional concerns drove the design, in that the tapered, lens-shaped plan arose from the client's desire for open floor areas serviced by centrally located lifts and corridors. The central core is set off to one side of the 20.4m (67ft) wide, 75.6m (248ft) long building to create sizable office spaces behind the glass curtain walls. Further away from the core, less corridor space is needed, so the plan tapers, most dramatically at the solid ends. Strikingly, these angled walls concealing exit stairs and vertical services do not meet; they retain an open-air gap between them.

Structure

The angled ends may appear to be the tower's main structure, but they are purely stiffeners for lateral loads. Instead, to support the slender building and brace it against lateral forces, Nervi designed a load-bearing reinforced-concrete frame with four central columns that taper in width and depth towards the top as the loads decrease. At the ground floor the columns are sizable shear walls; above this they are double, linked by beams. At the top-floor observation deck the outer columns stop short of the roof, which appears to float above a gap similar to those on the ends.

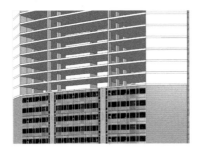

The core sits to one end of the shallow plan, creating a large open space in the middle of each floor.

Restoration

In April 2002, just seven months after the 9/11 atrocity, a single-engined plane accidentally slammed into the middle of the Pirelli Tower at the 26th floor, killing the pilot and two building occupants. The tragedy was the impetus for restoring the whole tower. Completed in 2010, the restoration gave the building a lustre d that had been missing in the intervening decades.

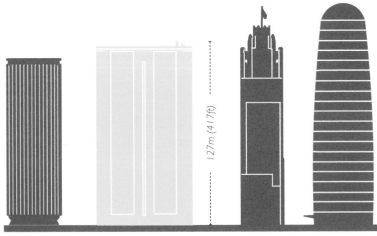

127m (417ft)

23

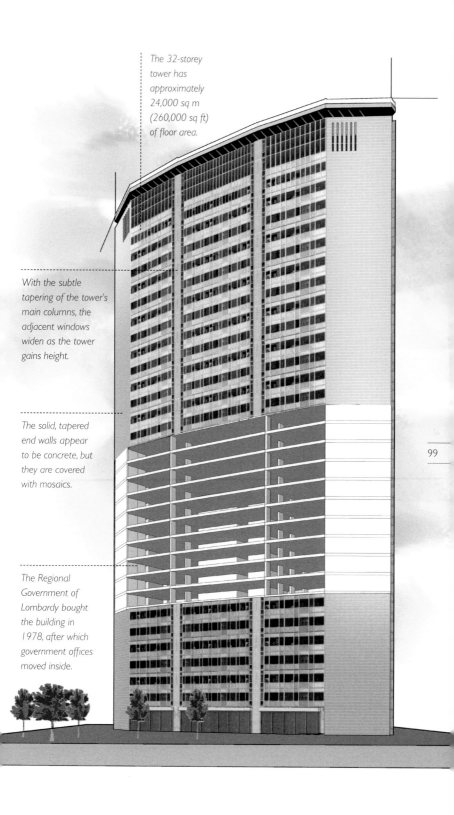

The 32-storey tower has approximately 24,000 sq m (260,000 sq ft) of floor area.

With the subtle tapering of the tower's main columns, the adjacent windows widen as the tower gains height.

The solid, tapered end walls appear to be concrete, but they are covered with mosaics.

The Regional Government of Lombardy bought the building in 1978, after which government offices moved inside.

99

TURNING TORSO

LOCATION: Malmö, Sweden | COMPLETION: 2005 | HEIGHT: 190m (623ft) | STOREYS: 57 | PRIMARY FUNCTIONS: Residential, offices OWNER/DEVELOPER: HSB Malmö | ARCHITECT AND STRUCTURAL ENGINEER: Santiago Calatrava Architects & Engineers | KEY FACTS: The first-ever twisting tower, and the tallest building in Scandinavia.

Towers and Bridges

Architect/engineer/artist Santiago Calatrava is known more for his bridges than his towers, but both have been widely influential. Just as his arched-suspension and cable-stayed bridges in his native Spain led to offshoots all over the world, it is hard to imagine the proliferation of twisted towers this century without Calatrava paving the way. The mixed-use Turning Torso was designed to anchor the transformation of Malmö's Western Harbour, the former shipbuilding yards located near the spectacular Øresund Bridge linking Sweden and Denmark.

Inspiration

As early as 1985 Calatrava was creating sculptures in his *Torso* series, where marble cubes suspended from string balance on chrome-plated steel spikes. The equally spaced cubes are stacked, stepped, alternating and – in the piece that sparked politician-turned-developer and HSB director Johnny Örbäck to hire him – twisting. Although Calatrava was hesitant at first about translating the seven twisting cubes of the 1.5m (5ft) tall *Turning Torso* into a full-scale building, Örbäck, set on making a Malmö landmark, convinced him.

Form

In translating the sculpture into a building, a number of changes occurred. Most obvious was the need for a core to house the lifts, stairs and vertical services. The number of cubes increased from seven to nine, each one consisting of five floors – the first two modules for office space and the remaining seven for 147 apartments. The plan changed from a square to a pentagon, or more accurately a triangle with straight sides appended to a square with convex sides. Two features of the original sculpture that were retained are the gaps between modules and the degree of turning from bottom to top: 90 degrees.

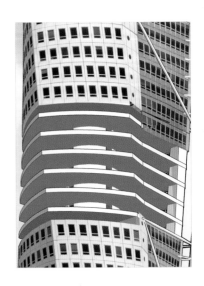

Mechanical services sit in the 2m (6½ft) tall gaps between some of the five-storey modules.

BUILDING AND STRUCTURE

An Innovative Structure

Given the practical need for the core, this circular element became the main structural component addressing vertical and lateral loads, as well as the point about which each floor rotates. The inner diameter is 10.6m (35ft) from bottom to top, though the thickness of the reinforced concrete walls varies from 2.5m (8ft) at the base to less than 0.5m (18in) at the roof. Concrete slabs are cantilevered out from the core, with additional support from steel perimeter columns; since these columns are discontinuous, the bottom floor of each module was thickened from the typical 25cm (10in) to 90cm (36in) to support the columns above and transfer their loads to the core. A reinforced concrete column at the tip of the triangle aids in supporting the floors and in resolving lateral drift from wind loads; the latter is further assisted by an exoskeleton of painted steel. Large diagonal and horizontal struts connect the exterior column, or spine, to a structural wall at the top of each module, while smaller struts tie it to each floor.

Façades

Two types of cladding cover the tower's modules: 2,800 curved aluminium panels on the three exposed sides, and 2,250 flat glass panels on the two sides behind the steel trusses. The leaning windows accentuate the twisting of the tower and do their part in turning it into one of the most unusual and unprecedented skyscrapers ever built.

Calatrava's tower sits atop a reflecting pool, so that visitors traverse a bridge to enter the building.

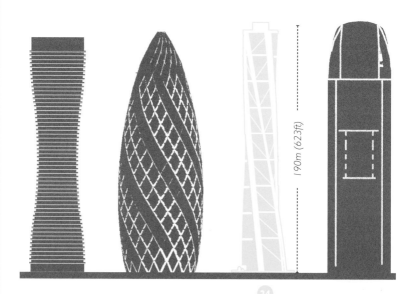

190m (623ft)

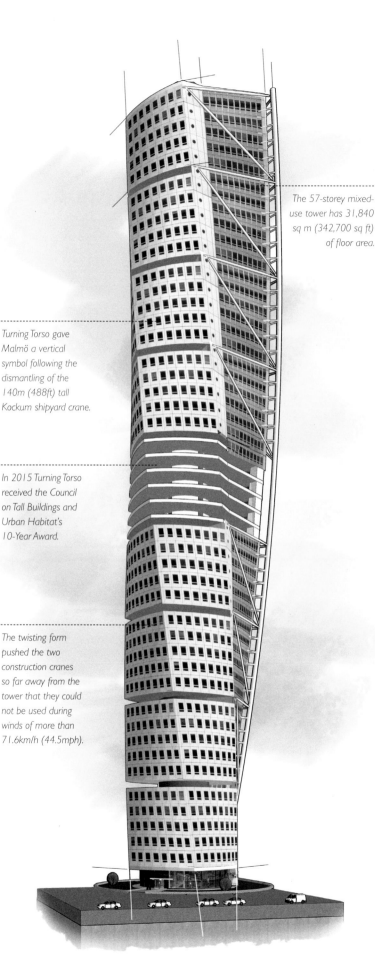

The 57-storey mixed-use tower has 31,840 sq m (342,700 sq ft) of floor area.

Turning Torso gave Malmö a vertical symbol following the dismantling of the 140m (488ft) tall Kockum shipyard crane.

In 2015 Turning Torso received the Council on Tall Buildings and Urban Habitat's 10-Year Award.

The twisting form pushed the two construction cranes so far away from the tower that they could not be used during winds of more than 71.6km/h (44.5mph).

PALACE OF CULTURE AND SCIENCE

LOCATION: Warsaw, Poland | **COMPLETION:** 1955 | **HEIGHT:** 231m (757ft) | **STOREYS:** 42 | **PRIMARY FUNCTIONS:** Cultural and recreational facilities, offices | **OWNER/DEVELOPER:** USSR, People's Republic of Poland **ARCHITECT:** Lev Rudnev | **STRUCTURAL ENGINEER:** Unknown **KEY FACTS:** The tallest building in both Warsaw and Poland. The tallest clock tower in the world until 2000.

Historical Context

Although the Palace of Culture and Science will be eclipsed as the tallest building in Warsawby by Norman Foster's Varso Tower in 2020, the 60-year-old structure is likely to remain the most iconic building on the skyline. Apart from the tower's ornate architectural design, it has become an integral part of Polish history and the country's identity following World War II and Communist rule.

The full name of the project was 'Palace of Culture and Science in the Name of Joseph Stalin'. Initiated in 1952, the building was a gift from the Soviet Union to Poland, but many Poles saw it as an imposition. Its architects, led by Lev Rudnev, and its style were Soviet, and all of the 4,000 workers who built the project came from the USSR, living in barracks on the edge of Warsaw. The Palace of Culture and Science (PKiN, from *Pałac Kultury i Nauki*) was completed in 1955, ten years after the end of the war but also two years after the death of Stalin, whose name was chiselled out of parts of the building after 1956, when his crimes were exposed and he was denounced by Soviet leader Nikita Khrushchev and Poland's own Władysław Gomułka.

The Site

PKiN was built as the centrepiece of the huge, 33-hectare (81.5-acre) Parade Square in the middle of Warsaw. At a time of national housing shortage, one hundred pre-war houses were razed and 4,000 people were displaced to realize the project. Eventually the parades made way for cars when the large space in front of the building's eastern façade was turned into a car park.

The highest occupied floor is at 160m (525ft), more than 70m (230ft) below the tower's architectural tip.

BUILDING AND STRUCTURE

Function

The most unique and ambitious aspect of PKiN is hinted at in its name: museums, cinemas, theatres, sports facilities and other public uses were the reason for its existence, not just offices. The imposing structure was built with 3,288 rooms, the largest – Congress Hall – able to accommodate nearly 3,000 spectators for Communist Party meetings in its early years and for rock concerts in later decades. Many of its original functions remain, though at one time PKiN was home to the largest casino in Poland.

Style

When built, Lev Rudnev's design was viewed locally as Soviet architectural tendencies overlaid with national traditions of Polish architecture. This came in part from the architect's tours of such central Polish towns as Sandomierz, Kraków and Toruń; historical details from these towns went into the ornamentation that festooned PKiN's exterior, particularly the spiky parapets. But beneath the stone façades and sculptures was a modern steel frame that the Soviets celebrated in propaganda, though it was already a fairly standard structural system in many parts of the world.

Although traditional in appearance, the masonry skin is hung on a steel frame, the norm in the mid-20th century.

Post-1989

After independence, Poland grappled with keeping or destroying 'Palec Stalina' (Stalin's Finger). Even with its negative connotations, the building was so prominent, distinctive and well used that it made more sense to keep it. The addition of clock faces atop the spire in 2000 cemented this decision and turned it, for a while, into the world's tallest timepiece.

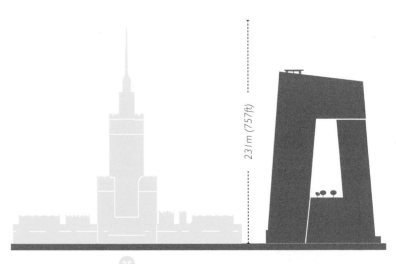

231m (757ft)

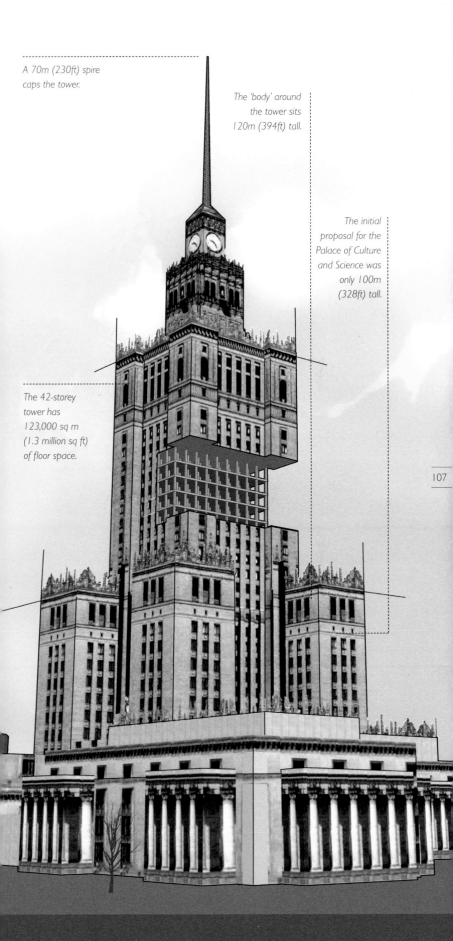

A 70m (230ft) spire caps the tower.

The 'body' around the tower sits 120m (394ft) tall.

The initial proposal for the Palace of Culture and Science was only 100m (328ft) tall.

The 42-storey tower has 123,000 sq m (1.3 million sq ft) of floor space.

107

ISTANBUL SAPPHIRE

LOCATION: Istanbul, Turkey | COMPLETION: 2010 | HEIGHT: 261m (856ft) | STOREYS: 55 | PRIMARY FUNCTION: Residential | OWNER/DEVELOPER: Biskon Yapı, Kiler GYO | ARCHITECT: Tabanlıoğlu Architects | STRUCTURAL ENGINEER: Balkar | KEY FACTS: Europe's tallest residential tower outside Moscow. The tallest building in Turkey.

Stacked Uses

This environmentally sustainable project, designed by Melkan Gürsel Tabanlıoğlu and Murat Tabanlıoğlu of their eponymous architecture firm, is made up of 187 apartments, 6 floors of retail, underground parking, and a public observation deck. The residential lobby begins five floors above ground level, and above the lobby the apartments are spread across four zones with nine or twelve storeys, separated by mechanical floors or full-floor common areas with recreation facilities. The design nurtures a feeling of togetherness often missing in high-rise living.

Gardens and Natural Ventilation

Each nine-storey residential zone is broken down further into three-storey groupings anchored at the lower levels by east-facing gardens. The gardens sit behind the outer glass wall, while the units are set back with their own sliding glass walls. The two floors above the gardens have balconies that project into the deep, three-storey-tall space; it is like living in a three-storey house with neighbours.

The gardens and double-wall façades introduce natural air into the living spaces. Due to the height, this outside air is cooler and therefore reduces the need for air conditioning. Louvred intake and exhaust vents open and close according to the weather.

Structure

Reinforced concrete is the primary structural material. Two rectangular cores are located at the north and south ends of the central, double-loaded corridor. The cores work with a grid of six shear walls perpendicular to the east and west façades. Steel columns supplement the concrete structure to support the exterior glass wall on the east façade. Steel beams and columns support a swooping roof above the mall – a communal space for the city.

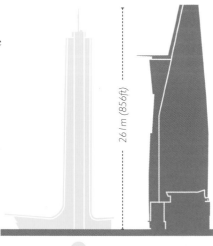

261m (856ft)

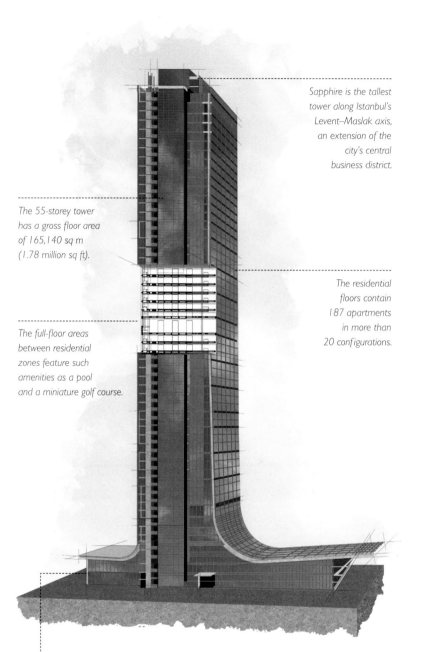

Sapphire is the tallest tower along Istanbul's Levent–Maslak axis, an extension of the city's central business district.

The 55-storey tower has a gross floor area of 165,140 sq m (1.78 million sq ft).

The full-floor areas between residential zones feature such amenities as a pool and a miniature golf course.

The residential floors contain 187 apartments in more than 20 configurations.

Six floors of parking, four underground floors of shopping and a direct connection to the subway required a pit excavated to 47.5m (511 ft) deep – reportedly Turkey's deepest excavation.

EVOLUTION TOWER

LOCATION: Moscow, Russia | COMPLETION: 2015 | HEIGHT: 246m (807ft)
STOREYS: 54 | PRIMARY FUNCTION: Offices | OWNER/DEVELOPER:
Snegiri Development, Transneft | ARCHITECT: Gorproject, RMJM
STRUCTURAL ENGINEER: GK-Techstroy, Gorproject | KEY FACTS:
The floor plan of the tower rotates 156 degrees from bottom to top.

False Start

The initial design of what would become Evolution Tower was unveiled in 2004, over 10 years before its eventual completion. As an integral part of the Moscow International Business Centre, or Moscow City – a large commercial development on the Presnenskaya embankment of the Moscow River – City Palace Tower, as it was called at the time, would have included a Wedding Palace with facilities for ceremonies. RMJM's architects, working with Scottish artist Karen Forbes, designed the competition-winning project as a spiral tower with a swooping glass 'bride's skirt' at its base and a dramatic concave roof capping the office tower.

A New Twist

In 2006 the tower gained planning permission and two years later a building permit, but the global financial crisis stalled the project. By the time it was resurrected in 2011, Moscow was no longer interested in a palace for weddings, particularly in a business area. Russia's Gorproject took over the project, which became solely an office tower. The base and the top were accordingly simplified, but the twist was retained. It was likened to a strand of DNA, hence the building's new name.

Moscow City

Although not the tallest tower in the dense, ongoing Moscow City development, Evolution Tower is one of the most visible, due in part to its form but also to its location: it is the southeasternmost tower of around a dozen which stand in a horseshoe arrangement around a central shopping mall, and is the closest to a pedestrian bridge over the river. The tower sits upon a landscaped podium with its own mall, a connection to the Metro, and a ceremonial staircase leading to the pedestrian bridge.

A helipad and observation deck sit between the twisted arches at the top of the tower.

BUILDING AND STRUCTURE

Structure

Evolution Tower twists clockwise three degrees per floor, totalling 156 degrees across its 54 floors. The square floor plates turn about the central core, though eight round columns in an octagonal arrangement extend through the whole tower vertically irrespective of the twisting. Four columns at the corners follow the twist and lean 14 degrees. At the roof these columns are capped by arches of steel – 41m (134½ft) spans with intermediate supports – that turn the twisting strands of the tower into closed loops.

The vertical (not leaning) orientation of the columns is apparent behind the glass façade.

Construction

The tower sits upon a 3.5m (11½ft) thick raft over a piled foundation; the raft was made with 8,000 cu m (283,000 cu ft) of concrete that was poured continuously over a 48-hour period. Construction of the all-reinforced-concrete, twisting structure was aided by a formwork system that enabled the core walls and floor slabs to be poured at the same time. A hydraulic self-climbing formwork followed the twist and enabled an average construction speed of seven days per floor.

Façade

A key to the tower's distinctive appearance is the reflective glass, which is curved to avoid a stepped appearance. Flat panes of glass were cold-bent into the twisted aluminium frames to achieve these curves. Adjacent glass façades are treated differently – all reflective on two sides and with white stripes on the other two – to accentuate the tower's twist while subtly referring to the original symbolism of a bride and groom embracing each other.

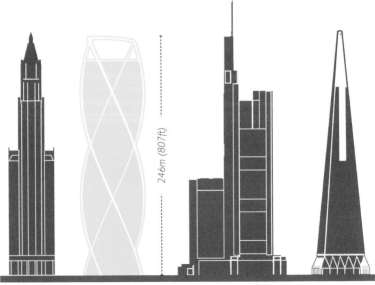

246m (807ft)

27

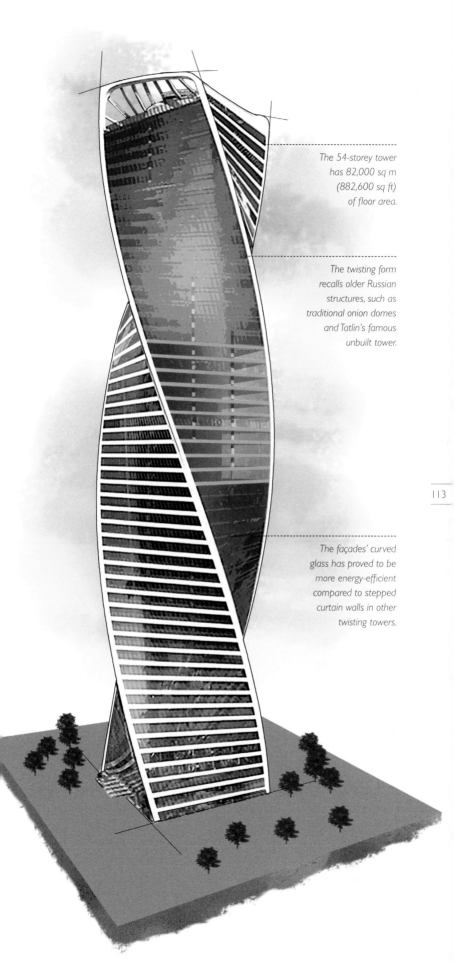

The 54-storey tower has 82,000 sq m (882,600 sq ft) of floor area.

The twisting form recalls older Russian structures, such as traditional onion domes and Tatlin's famous unbuilt tower.

The façades' curved glass has proved to be more energy-efficient compared to stepped curtain walls in other twisting towers.

113

BAHRAIN WORLD TRADE CENTER

LOCATION: Manama, Bahrain | **COMPLETION:** 2008 | **HEIGHT:** 240m (787ft) | **STOREYS:** 45 | **PRIMARY FUNCTION:** Offices | **OWNER/ DEVELOPER:** Bahrain World Trade Center, Kingdom of Bahrain **ARCHITECT AND STRUCTURAL ENGINEER:** Atkins | **KEY FACTS:** The first building to integrate large-scale wind turbines.

After Oil

Manama is the capital and largest city of the Kingdom of Bahrain, an island country that has been highly dependent upon oil and natural gas since the middle of last century. This century, the country has invested in tourism and financial services, the latter being concentrated mainly in Manama. A symbol of Bahrain's view towards a post-oil future are the two towers of the Bahrain World Trade Center (BWTC), which hold three 29m (95ft) diameter wind turbines in the gap between them.

Concept

From the project's start in 2004, the BWTC was meant to rejuvenate a 30-year-old hotel and shopping mall on a prominent site in Manama's central business district overlooking the Arabian Gulf to the north. The brief included the extension of the mall and parking, with the addition of 50,000 sq m (538,000 sq ft) of office space. Shaun Killa of Atkins, the firm responsible for the sail-like Burj Al Arab in the UAE (page 126), led the design of the BWTC. As an avid sailing enthusiast, Killa looked for inspiration to the aerodynamics of sailing boats; he was also impressed by traditional Arab wind towers which were used to cool houses by creating updraughts. On an early visit to the project site, the architect noticed the constant breezes coming off the Gulf, and this led him to propose the two towers hoisting wind turbines.

Three wind turbines are sited between the two towers. Each turbine's nacelle with its equipment weighs 10 tonnes (9.8 tons).

BUILDING AND STRUCTURE

Aerodynamics

Atkins shaped the plans of the two 50-storey towers like aerofoils, to funnel the winds but also to accelerate the wind speed through the gap by exploiting the negative pressure on the leeward side of the buildings. Two Danish companies, the engineering and design consultancy Ramboll and the wind turbine company Norwin, carried out wind-tunnel tests to determine the ideal wind direction and range. To maintain the same wind velocity across all three turbines, the towers taper towards their tips where the breezes are naturally stronger.

The Turbines

To make the integration of wind turbines economically feasible, conventional technologies were used: horizontal turbines normally found in the fields of Denmark where they would be orientated to prevailing breezes. Positioned at 60, 96 and 132m (197, 315 and 433ft) above ground, the turbines and their nacelles (housings for generator, gearbox, controls and other systems) are mounted on bridges that span 31.7m 104ft) from tower to tower.

The towers sit atop a three-storey base that connects to an existing shopping mall.

The bridges are shaped in a shallow 'V' to allow for any deflection of the blades caused by the wind, and they are attached to the towers with rubber bearings to isolate movement from the turbines so the tenants are not impacted. The nominal 225kW turbines, in operation since 2009 after one year of testing, produce 11 to 15 per cent of the project's electricity. In concert with other green building features, the turbines have made the BWTC a desirable address and a symbol of sustainability in a region not normally associated with it.

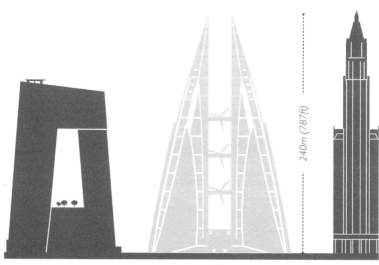

240m (787ft)

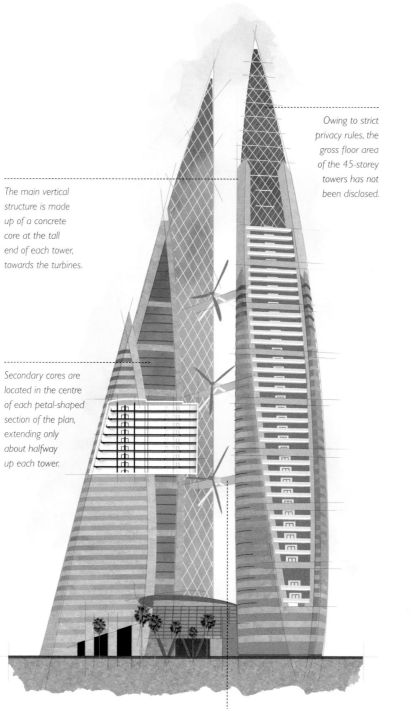

The main vertical structure is made up of a concrete core at the tall end of each tower, towards the turbines.

Secondary cores are located in the centre of each petal-shaped section of the plan, extending only about halfway up each tower.

Owing to strict privacy rules, the gross floor area of the 45-storey towers has not been disclosed.

Three systems – two in the turbines and one in the buildings – monitor the turbines for safety, shutting them down in adverse weather or other situations.

AL BAHR TOWERS

LOCATION: Abu Dhabi, UAE | COMPLETION: 2012 | HEIGHT: 145m (476ft) | STOREYS: 29 | PRIMARY FUNCTION: Offices | OWNER/ DEVELOPER: Abu Dhabi Investment Council (ADIC) | ARCHITECT: Aedas, Diar Consult | STRUCTURAL ENGINEER: Arup | KEY FACTS: Each tower features over 1,000 movable façade elements.

Historical Precedents

All too often, the skyscraper booms in Abu Dhabi and Dubai in this century have seen the importation of designs whose forms and exteriors are alien to the desert context of the UAE. A refreshing exception is the twin towers that Aedas's London office designed for the ADIC, an investment arm of the Government of Abu Dhabi, in a 2007 competition. With a mandate from the client for a strong sustainability agenda, the architects envisioned the glass towers cloaked in a shading system inspired by traditional Arabic pierced screens called *mashrabiyas*. A modern precedent – retractable canopies designed by Germany's SL Rasch for the Prophet's Mosque in Medina, Saudi Arabia – pointed the way towards a dynamic façade.

Biomimicry

Over the course of a day, the computer-controlled outer façades of the Al Bahr Towers gradually open and close once in response to the path of the sun. Sensors allow this flower-like movement of the façade elements to change as needed due to variations in sun and wind. The glass wall, 2m (6½ft) behind the dynamic façade, is exposed along the north elevation, where the sun does not hit.

Mashrabiyas

Each of the movable mashrabiya units – 1,049 per tower – is made up of six triangular PTFE-coated fibreglass fabric panels mounted on a Y-shaped tripod. Together these panels define a larger, one-storey-high triangle, and the orientation of these triangles alternates so that they lock together into a dense folded pattern across the curving façades. When the mashrabiyas open, the central piece of the tripod pushes out and the panels fold in; there are five intermediate steps between fully closed and fully open. The mesh panels are designed to transmit roughly 40 per cent of visible light, resulting in a 35 per cent reduction in annual cooling loads. In conjunction with other 'green' building features devised by Arup, this enables the towers to emit 40 per cent less carbon than comparable buildings elsewhere.

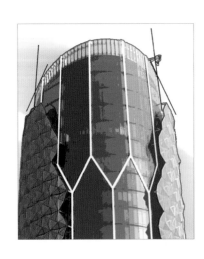

An angled roof – like a tube of lipstick – houses photovoltaic panels and gives the cylindrical buildings their distinctive profiles.

BUILDING AND STRUCTURE

Testing

Active façades are not common, so thorough testing was needed to determine that the mashrabiyas would function properly and hold up over time. Chinese curtain wall manufacturer Yuanda took care of both the glass curtain wall and the mashrabiyas, subjecting them to hours of sand, wind, salt water and heat. Their tests of the mock-up in China were followed by further tests of the same on site. It is expected that the actuators and motors will last about 15 and 10 years, respectively, before replacement is needed.

Structure

Although the twin towers appear to be simple cylinders that rise from a two-storey podium, they actually bow out slightly in the middle floors. Furthermore, while the core is circular, the perimeter is more like an ellipse – a combination of geometries intended to minimize solar exposure. Steel beams extend column-free from

On the north elevation, where no sunshades are needed, the diagrid bracing is exposed.

the 20.3m (66½ft) diameter core to the perimeter structure of steel columns arranged in a honeycomb geometry, which is visible externally on the northern face of each tower. This alone would make the towers handsome but unremarkable; but with the addition of the operable shades, they are a futuristic creation that is nevertheless rooted in tradition.

145m (476ft)

A number of four-storey-tall sky gardens are located on the south façades behind the movable mashrabiyas.

The two 29-storey towers have 56,000 sq m (603,000 sq ft) of floor area.

The pair of towers sits upon a two-storey plinth that contains parking, mechanical and storage in the basement and entrance, auditorium and prayer rooms above ground between the buildings. Above the podium is a landscaped deck.

The building owner, ADIC, incorporates the towers' mashrabiya design into its logo.

KINGDOM CENTRE

LOCATION: Riyadh, Saudi Arabia | COMPLETION: 2002 | HEIGHT: 302m (992ft) | STOREYS: 41 | PRIMARY FUNCTIONS: Residential, hotel, offices OWNER/DEVELOPER: Kingdom Holding Company | ARCHITECT: Ellerbe Becket, Omrania & Associates | STRUCTURAL ENGINEER: Arup | KEY FACTS: Not the tallest tower in Riyadh, but the most recognizable. Winner of Emporis Skyscraper Award in 2002 as best new skyscraper of the year.

Competition

Prince Alwaleed bin Talal Abdulaziz Al Saud, grandson of King Abdulaziz, the founder of Saudi Arabia, had high hopes for Kingdom Centre in Riyadh: he wanted the tower to be as recognized globally as the Eiffel Tower. Although roughly the same height as the Parisian landmark, Kingdom Centre is a very different entity, the outcome of a design competition involving more than 100 proposals over a three-year period.

Building Form

Prince Alwaleed requested a simple, monolithic, symmetrical structure that would be more global than regional, and the international team of US architecture firm Ellerbe Becket (now AECOM) and Riyadh's Omrania & Associates won with an attention-getting, curved glass tower topped by a triangular opening and an enclosed bridge. This strong statement was aided in part by siting the project at a distance from the dense King Abdullah Financial District, so that it towers over its predominantly low-scale surroundings (in recent years it has been joined by taller buildings, but none as tall as Kingdom Centre itself). The architects were able to push the tower higher than the planning ordinance's 30-storey height limit since the parabolic opening is sculptural, free of occupied floors, and therefore allowable.

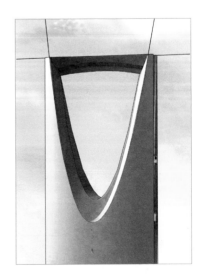

The observation deck spanning the opening has an arched floor below the level roof.

BUILDING AND STRUCTURE

Structure

Given the shape of the tower's plan – like an almond with notched ends – all of the occupied floors are framed in reinforced concrete. The structure of the top third of the building is tubular steel, and it is connected to the concrete floors below by two-storey-tall, high-strength anchor bars. The tower sits upon a concrete mat foundation that bears directly on rock.

Façade

Despite these two distinct structural systems, the convex and notched surfaces of the exterior are clad in a uniform glass façade of butt-glazed silver reflective glass. From a distance the joints between the glass panes disappear, turning the tower into a mirror with distorted reflections of the sky and its surroundings. Variation is found at the triangular opening with its inverted catenary arch, where aluminium panels the same size as the glass panes serve as a canvas for coloured lights mounted to the underside of the bridge. Lastly, the unoccupied floors adjacent to the opening are given over to a grid of lights in the evening hours, bringing even more attention to the prince's architectural statement.

Function

Kingdom Centre actually consists of three elements totalling 185,000 sq m (2 million sq ft): the tower, the east podium and the west podium. The tower sits between the two podiums, rather than on top of them, while formal gardens occupy the spaces on the north and south sides of the tower. The east podium contains a shopping mall, the west podium has wedding, conference and sports facilities, and the tower is given over to a five-star hotel, the headquarters of Kingdom Holding Company, and the arched observation deck at the

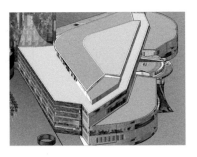

The elliptical plan of the tower is reiterated in other elements, such as the entrances on the north side.

top, where angled glass walls give views of the city and glimpses of the base of the project itself. A prayer room is provided in the tower, and within the mall is a floor reserved for women, where veils are not required. The three main elements sit above a 3,000-car underground parking garage.

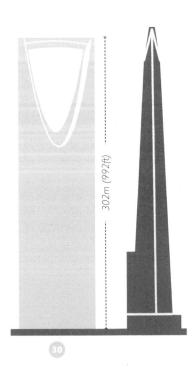

302m (992ft)

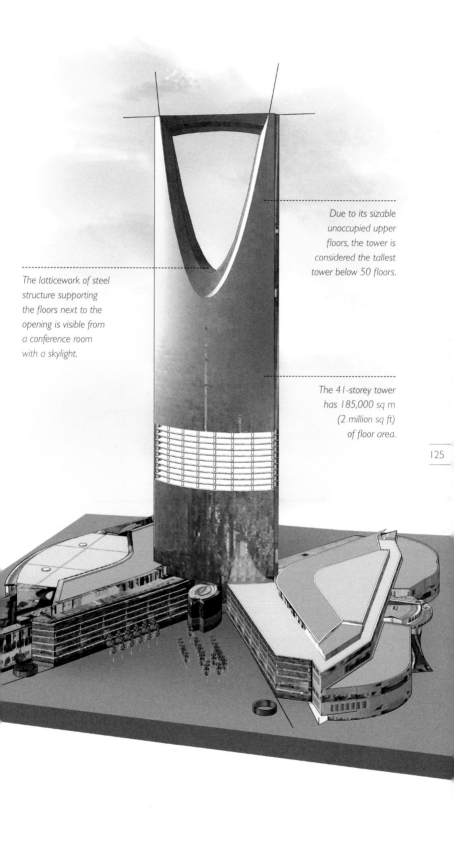

The latticework of steel structure supporting the floors next to the opening is visible from a conference room with a skylight.

Due to its sizable unoccupied upper floors, the tower is considered the tallest tower below 50 floors.

The 41-storey tower has 185,000 sq m (2 million sq ft) of floor area.

BURJ
AL ARAB

LOCATION: Dubai, UAE | COMPLETION: 1999 | HEIGHT: 321m (1,053ft)
STOREYS: 56 | PRIMARY FUNCTION: Hotel | OWNER/DEVELOPER:
Jumeirah Group International | ARCHITECT: Atkins | STRUCTURAL
ENGINEERS: Atkins, e.construct | KEY FACTS: The world's tallest atrium,
at 180m (590ft). Claims to be the only seven-star hotel in the world.

Designing an Icon

When Atkins was hired in 1993
for the design, engineering and
construction management of two
hotels for the Jumeirah Group, one
of these had to become an icon that
would say, 'Welcome to Dubai.'
Naturally this role would fall to the
tower built on an artificial island in
the Persian Gulf, rather than the
lower, 'beached' hotel it would
overlook. For British architect Tom
Wright of Atkins, inspiration was
found in modern sailing boats, so that
the final design resembles a sail blown
by the wind. It satisfies Wright's 'icon
test': can it, like the Sydney Opera
House, be drawn in five seconds and
be instantly recognizable?

The Site

Burj Al Arab is located about 15km
(9¼ miles) southwest of the centre
of Dubai and another icon, the Burj
Khalifa (page 134). Not much was
there in the mid-1990s, apart from
the Chicago Beach Hotel, which was
demolished once the two new hotels
were complete. Now both stand in
the midst of the booming metropolis,
and the triangular island (expanded
in 2016 to a bow-tie shape) is
minuscule compared to the tree-
shaped Palm Jumeirah and other
pieces of land reclaimed from the sea.

Island Construction

Five major steps were involved in the
construction of the island that would
support the 56-storey hotel. First,
sheet-pile walls matching the
footprint were driven into the sand
and supported by temporary piles and
cables. Second, sand was used to fill
inside the sheet piles and rocks were
placed outside for support. Third, the
substructure's 230 piles, 1.5m (5ft) in
diameter, were driven 45m (148ft)
into the seabed. Fourth, SHED units
(hollow blocks that dissipate the
waves) were installed atop the rocks.
Fifth, the sand was removed to expose
the piles, build a concrete 'bathtub'
and then start the superstructure.
It took one year to build the island,
which sits 7m (23ft) above the surface
of the water to protect the hotel from
a 100-year storm (a storm that has a
1 per cent chance of occurring in any
given year).

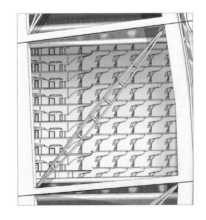

*Removing one row of the hotel rooms reveals
the full-height atrium that sits behind the sail-
like fabric façade on the right.*

BUILDING AND STRUCTURE

Plan

In plan, the Burj Al Arab is a 'V' composed of hotel suites in two wings with a triangular atrium between them. The opening facing the shore to the southeast is covered by a huge double-layer PTFE fabric wall that cuts down on direct sunlight. The core, with its lifts and other vertical services, is located at the V's apex. Atop the building are two special cantilevered structures: a helipad facing the beach, which provides an alternative to driving to the island over the bridge, and a restaurant facing the water.

Structure

Given the V-shaped plan and distinctive swoop of the building, Atkins developed a hybrid structure. Vertical loads are taken care of by the concrete core, floor slabs and shear walls at the hotel suites. Arcing steel exoskeletons with huge diagonal trusses stabilize the building from north–south winds, while east–west lateral forces are addressed by huge cross braces that sit behind the fabric 'sail'. This last piece, which is supported by curved steel trusses hung from the top of the atrium, is the most overt reference to the sailing inspiration, but it is just one of many elements that harmonize into one of the most memorable skyscrapers of recent years.

A restaurant facing the water on the left and the helipad on the right sit below the 60m (196ft) tall mast and the curving structure at the top of the building.

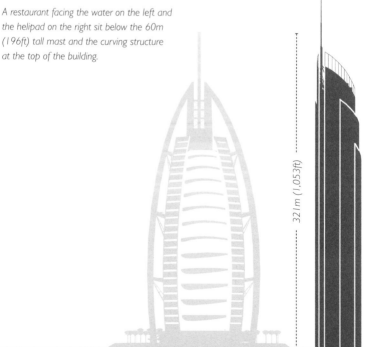

321m (1,053ft)

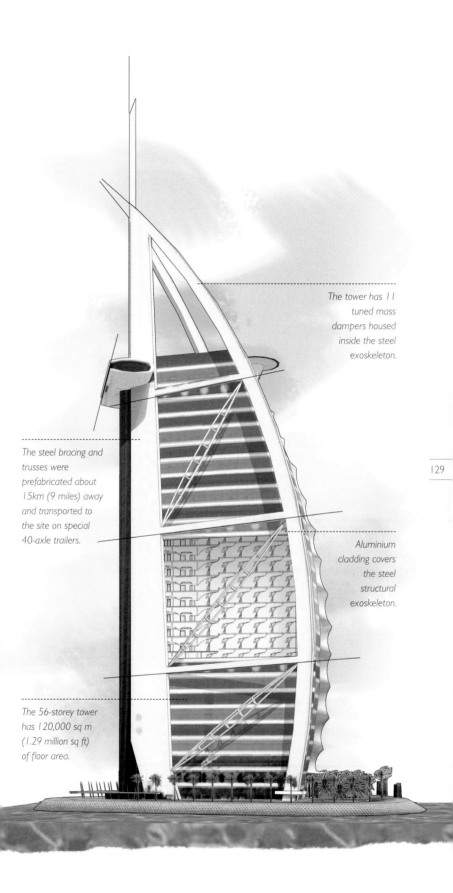

The tower has 11 tuned mass dampers housed inside the steel exoskeleton.

The steel bracing and trusses were prefabricated about 15km (9 miles) away and transported to the site on special 40-axle trailers.

Aluminium cladding covers the steel structural exoskeleton.

The 56-storey tower has 120,000 sq m (1.29 million sq ft) of floor area.

129

O-14

LOCATION: Dubai, UAE | COMPLETION: 2010 | HEIGHT: 106m (347ft)
STOREYS: 24 | PRIMARY FUNCTION: Offices | OWNER/DEVELOPER:
H&H Investment and Development | ARCHITECT: Reiser + Umemoto,
RUR Architecture, Erga Progress | STRUCTURAL ENGINEER: Ysrael A
Seinuk KEY FACTS: The tower's primary structure – an undulating porous
concrete wall – is placed outside the building rather than in its core.

Site History

Business Bay is an ongoing mixed-use development straddling an extension of Dubai Creek just south of Downtown Dubai and the Burj Khalifa. The site infrastructure was in place by 2008, but since the work unfortunately coincided with the global economic collapse, the build-out of the planned 7.4 million sq m (80 million sq ft) of offices and residences has been slow. One of the few towers erected along the waterway occupies lot BB.A05.O14, from which it takes its name.

Commission

The choice of Jesse Reiser and Nanako Umemoto – two academic, theoretically minded New York architects with few built projects to their credit – is a bold one for a speculative office tower. The partners came to the attention of Shahab Lutfi Harmoozi, one half of H&H, when they lost a competition for a Business Bay tower to the famed British-Iranian architect Zaha Hadid. The fact that one of the developer's own employees had studied under Reiser helped to secure this unconventional choice.

Building Form

RUR fittingly departed from convention with two broad strokes. First, they convinced H&H to bury underground the four-storey parking podium required by Business Bay's master plan; this resulted in an elevated two-storey podium with extra office space wrapping the tower on three sides and shading a plaza overlooking the creek. Second, rejecting an amorphous design that was too technically complicated, they developed a double-layer structure that turned the office tower inside out: Structure and skin flipped by way of an undulating concrete exoskeleton – a square tube pinched at the sides and rounded at the corners – with an apparently random pattern of openings shading tinted window walls.

The exterior wall extends past the roof by the equivalent of two storeys.

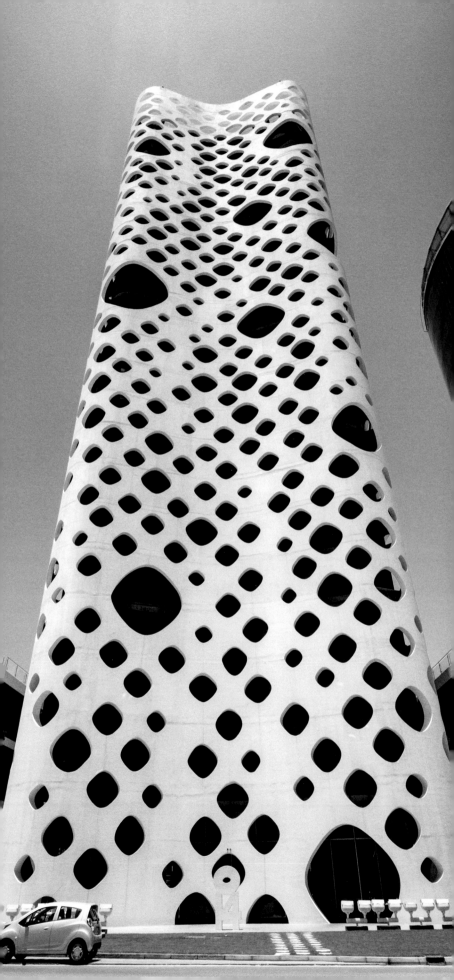

BUILDING AND STRUCTURE

Structure

The attention-getting form and wrapper is more than just a means of making the building stand out within a mega-development catering to an anticipated hundreds of thousands of residents and employees. The concrete exoskeleton takes care of the majority of gravity and lateral loads, frees up the core from its usual structural role, minimizes the depth of the concrete floor plates that would normally transfer vertical loads to the core and eliminates columns between the exterior wall and the core. It does this through a diagrid. Yet, unlike such expressive steel structures as 30 St Mary Axe and Canton Tower (pages 84 and 152), O-14 buries its diagrid within the concrete. Hints of the miles of reinforcing bars corresponding to the diagonal forces are visible in the diagonal pattern of the lozenge-shaped openings, which range in size from 1.4m (4½ft) to 8.3m (27¼ft) and intentionally confuse a reading of the floors behind them, except at the few multistorey openings.

Construction

Given the extruded form of the exoskeleton, a slip-form technique with modular steel concrete forms was employed. The voids in five sizes were created with CNC-cut polystyrene foam forms lined with melamine laminate. The wall was cast with superliquid concrete, resulting in a seamless wrapper whose unusual appearance stands out among Dubai's numerous much taller skyscrapers.

A detached podium wraps the sides and back of the structure so the tower reaches to the ground when seen from the street.

ASIA

132

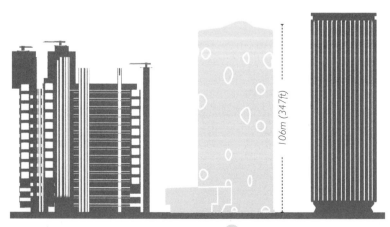

106m (347ft)

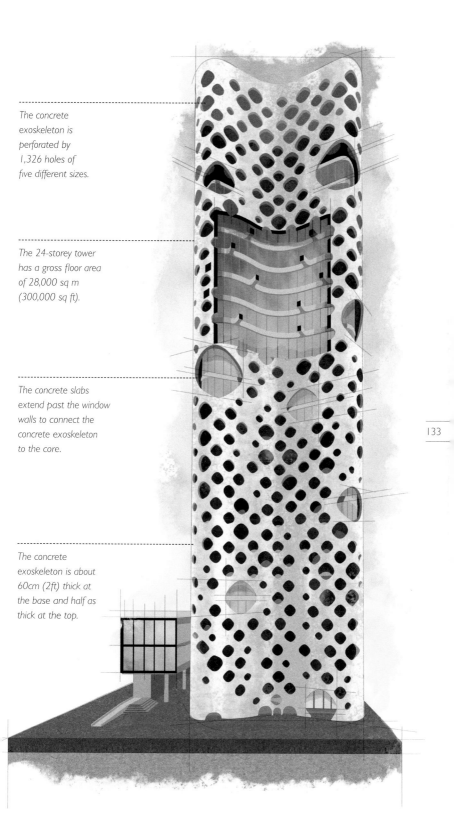

The concrete exoskeleton is perforated by 1,326 holes of five different sizes.

The 24-storey tower has a gross floor area of 28,000 sq m (300,000 sq ft).

The concrete slabs extend past the window walls to connect the concrete exoskeleton to the core.

The concrete exoskeleton is about 60cm (2ft) thick at the base and half as thick at the top.

133

BURJ KHALIFA

LOCATION: Dubai, UAE | COMPLETION: 2010 | HEIGHT: 828m (2,717ft)
STOREYS: 63 | PRIMARY FUNCTIONS: Office, residential, hotel
OWNER/DEVELOPER: Emaar Properties | ARCHITECTS: Skidmore,
Owings & Merrill (SOM), Hyder Consulting | STRUCTURAL ENGINEERS:
SOM, Hyder Consulting | KEY FACTS: The world's tallest building, nearly
twice the height of the Empire State Building. The first 'megatall' tower.

World's Tallest

From the moment Emaar Properties
started planning a large mixed-use
development with residential, hotel,
office and shopping facilities in the
centre of Dubai, its centrepiece was
intended to become the world's tallest
building. The competition-winning
scheme by SOM's Adrian Smith
topped the then champion, Taipei
101 (page 172) by only around 10m
(33ft), a distance that was in line with
the incremental growth of supertall
skyscrapers (those over 300m/984ft)
since as far back as the Empire State
Building in 1931. But when the Burj
Khalifa opened eight years later, in
January 2010, its official height
would surpass its predecessors by
such a wide margin that a new
beast was born: the 'megatall' (over
600m/1,968ft).

Building Form

At these stratospheric heights, the
design of megatalls is equal parts
architecture and engineering, yet
Smith's inspirations were natural
and historical: the desert flower
Hymenocallis and traditional Islamic
architecture. These mostly informed
the plan, the former defining its radial
'Y' shape, and the latter articulated in
the bay-like windows that correspond
to the stepping form.

*The tower's 'vanity height' (from its highest
occupied floor to its architectural tip) is
244m (800ft).*

Wind Engineering

The process that pushed SOM's
design from an ambitious supertall to
an unprecedented megatall started in
the wind tunnel, where their initial
design performed poorly. Smith and
SOM structural engineer William
Baker revised the design, only to
discover that this enabled them to
build higher than first planned. How
high exactly would be unknown until
near completion, since the official
height was kept under wraps, lest any
competitors try to best it during the
long years of construction. Design
was as much a consideration as any,
though, as Smith sought the ideal
way to terminate the tower with its
progressive, spiralling setbacks.

BUILDING AND STRUCTURE

Buttressed Core

The giant leap forward was enabled by Baker's 'buttressed core' structure. Each wing is made up of concrete corridor walls, perpendicular shear walls and perimeter columns that are buttressed to the six-sided central core – like a large tripod. The structure strongly resists lateral and torsional (twisting) forces but is aided by five sets of outriggers located at double-height mechanical floors distributed evenly up the building. Additionally, the columns at the tip of each wing are located atop shear walls, eliminating the need for column transfers at the setbacks, which happen every seven floors. The concrete structure reaches level 156, above which a steel bracing system supports the decorative spire and mast that provide the satisfying apex Smith wanted.

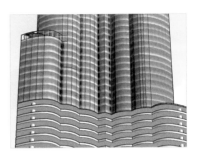

The tower's orientation, setbacks and mullions all contribute towards reducing the wind acting upon the building.

Construction

Burj Khalifa sits on a 6.7m (12ft) concrete raft supported by 194 bored, cast-in-place piles 1.5m (5ft) in diameter and about 43m 141ft) deep. Foundation work was wrapped up in February 2005, and the superstructure reached level 100 by the first month of 2007. This speed was enabled by at least two innovations put in place by the contractor, Samsung: auto-climbing formwork and advances in pumps for pushing concrete to record heights – just one more record among so many.

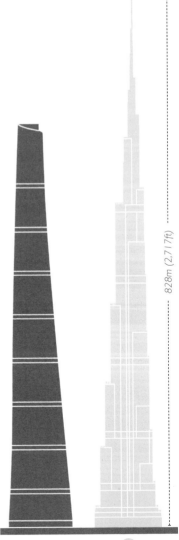

828m (2,717ft)

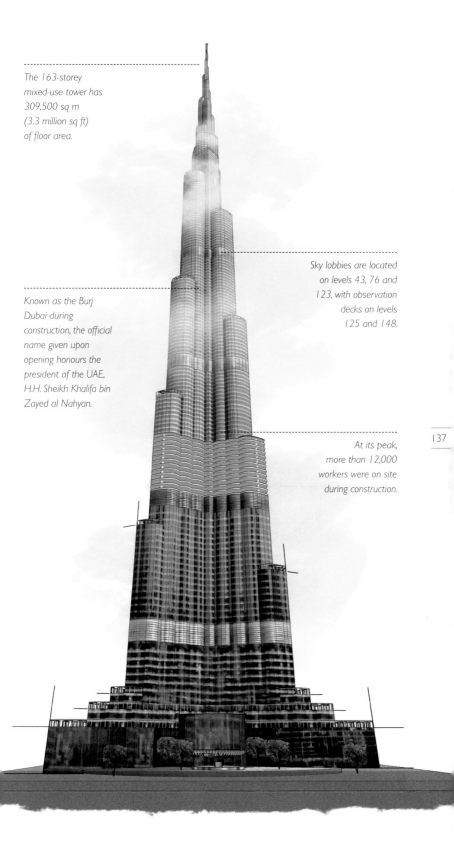

The 163-storey mixed-use tower has 309,500 sq m (3.3 million sq ft) of floor area.

Sky lobbies are located on levels 43, 76 and 123, with observation decks on levels 125 and 148.

Known as the Burj Dubai during construction, the official name given upon opening honours the president of the UAE, H.H. Sheikh Khalifa bin Zayed al Nahyan.

At its peak, more than 12,000 workers were on site during construction.

MAHANAKHON

LOCATION: Bangkok, Thailand | **COMPLETION:** 2016 | **HEIGHT:** 314m (1,031ft) | **STORIES:** 75 | **PRIMARY FUNCTIONS:** Residential, hotel
OWNER/DEVELOPER: PACE Development Corporation | **ARCHITECTS:** Büro Ole Scheeren, Hok Lok Siew Design, Office for Metropolitan Architecture (OMA) | **STRUCTURAL ENGINEERS:** Arup, Bouygues Thai
KEY FACTS: The tallest building in Thailand.

Great Metropolis

MahaNakhon, which means 'Great Metropolis' in Thai, is located in the Silom business district of Bangkok, Thailand's most populous city with over 8 million people (nearly 15 million in the greater metropolitan area). The project is sited next to a Skytrain station and a planned BRT (bus rapid transit) stop, making it ideal for a mix of uses.

Mixed Uses

PACE's aim was to provide three financially independent elements in order to increase the odds of a successful development: residential, hotel and retail. The bulk of the tower is residential, with 207 units in special Ritz-Carlton Residences; floors 23–54 feature standard units, while 54–73 provide larger 'Sky Residences'. At the base of the tower is the 150-room Edition Hotel, a collaboration between Marriott and American hotelier Ian Schrager. Retail is located in MahaNakhon CUBE, a detached low-rise volume that defines MahaNakhon Square between it and the tower. Public facilities are also found atop the tower: an observatory floors on 74 and 75, and the Sky Bar on 76 and 77.

Pixelated Ribbon

Architect Ole Scheeren – who had previously worked for OMA on such projects as CCTV Headquarters in Beijing (page 160) and started this design while employed there – conceptualized the tower as a 'boring' extrusion of a square plan that was made 'lively' through the introduction of a three-dimensional ribbon of 'pixels' that wraps the whole height of the tower. Apparently carving away at the rectilinear mass to reveal the skyscraper's inner life, the ribbon is composed of terraces for the tower's occupants.

The unconventional form of the tower required wind-tunnel tests to be done from 36 directions.

BUILDING AND STRUCTURE

Structure

The tower's main feature – the pixelated ribbon – meant that continuous columns could not be located at the perimeter of the square plan, which has a dimension of approximately 39m (128ft) per side; to allow room for the terraces, the columns would need to be located closer to the core. This led the structural engineers to design an all-reinforced-concrete structure with a tapering core (23m/75 ft square at grade and 23 × 14m/75 × 46ft at the top), 12 megacolumns (three per side), floor slabs, and three double-height outrigger trusses at levels 19–20, 35–36 and 51–52. The placement of the megacolumns is roughly halfway between core and exterior, so that half of the vertical load is taken up by the core and half by the megacolumns; the outriggers shift this distribution 70:30 towards the stronger core while improving the tower's lateral stiffness. The whole structure sits upon a mat foundation

The 'pixel' residences fetched prices 10% higher than those of 'non-pixel' residences.

8.75m (28¾ft) thick, which in turn sits upon 129 piles drilled to depths of 65m (213ft) to allow for the area's soft soils.

Observatory

The two-storey indoor observatory atop MahaNakhon is considered, like the tower itself, the highest in Thailand. But this century, height takes a back seat to thrills. Enter the 'Sky Tray', a glass-floored open-air platform at the tower's roof that invites visitors to 'walk on air' 314m (1,031ft) above the rest of Bangkok.

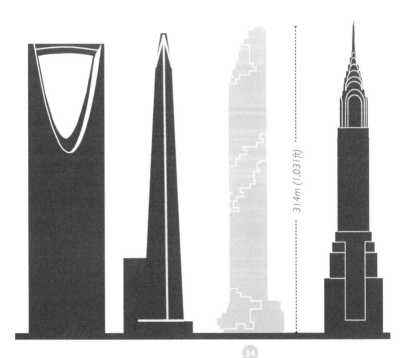

314m (1,031ft)

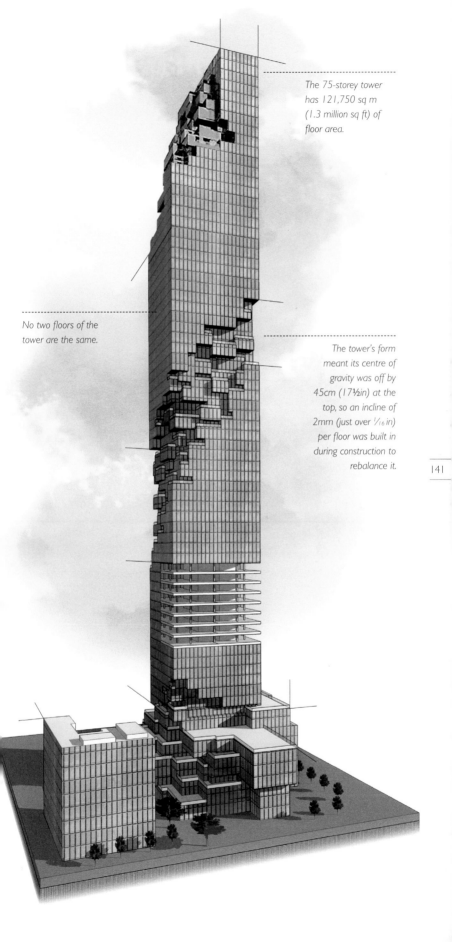

The 75-storey tower has 121,750 sq m (1.3 million sq ft) of floor area.

No two floors of the tower are the same.

The tower's form meant its centre of gravity was off by 45cm (17½in) at the top, so an incline of 2mm (just over ¹⁄₁₆ in) per floor was built in during construction to rebalance it.

PETRONAS TWIN TOWERS

LOCATION: Kuala Lumpur, Malaysia | **COMPLETION:** 1998
HEIGHT: 452m (1,483ft) | **STOREYS:** 88 | **PRIMARY FUNCTION:** Offices
OWNER/DEVELOPER: KLCC Property Holdings | **ARCHITECTS:** César
Pelli & Associates, Adamson Associates | **STRUCTURAL ENGINEERS:**
Thornton Tomasetti, Ranhill Bersekutu | **KEY FACTS:** Tallest building
in the world from 1998 until 2004.

Competition

In the 1980s the Selangor Turf Club
moved to the outskirts of Kuala
Lumpur, opening up a 40-hectare
(100-acre) site in the central 'Golden
Triangle' commercial district. Klages,
Carter, Vail & Partners developed the
site's master plan: a large central park
surrounded by offices, apartments
and hotels. In 1991 a competition
was held to design a pair of office
towers for Petronas, the national
petroleum company. Architect César
Pelli won with a design that strove to
create a recognizable gateway,
achieved through sculptural forms
and a symmetrical space between the
two towers.

East and West

The aim of the competition was not
to create the world's tallest buildings,
but when the Petronas Twin Towers
were completed in 1998 they
displaced Chicago's Sears – now
Willis – Tower (page 28), which had
held the top position for 34 years.
Although the twins were to lose their
crown a scant six years later, they
marked a shift from West to East in
building tall. Appropriately, Pelli's
design is a synthesis of West and East
– the former contributing technology
and the historical ambition to soar
higher and higher, and the latter
bringing Islamic geometries and a
stepped profile referencing Malaysia's
traditional architecture.

*The towers step back five times on the way
to their pointed tops.*

BUILDING AND STRUCTURE

Design

The symmetrical plan of each tower was generated by overlaying two squares of the same size, the second rotated at 45 degrees to the first. The resulting perimeter, with eight outside corners, was inefficient in itself but was made usable by adding semicircular bulges at each inside corner. Sixteen reinforced-concrete columns at each inside corner define a ring that is echoed in the circular concrete core (haunched concrete beams connect the two). On the outside, each glassy floor is wrapped in four horizontal projections, all in stainless steel: two teardrop-shaped sunshades near the top of the vision glazing and two circular bands at the spandrel. These lines, though modern in material and construction, seem to accentuate the plan's Eastern motifs while giving the towers a glistening presence at any time of day.

Skybridge

Linking the two towers at their 41st and 42nd floors is a bridge that reinforces the project's gateway aspect by drawing attention to the space between the towers. But the bridge, which coincides with sky lobbies for the upper floors, is functional: It acts as a means of emergency egress and therefore reduces the area needed for stairs at lower floors. The double-decker bridge (echoing the towers' double-decker elevators) is supported on an arch of hollow steel columns; Teflon pads and expansion joints allow the bridge to move as the towers move.

Construction

Between design completion and construction start, the structural engineers at Thornton Tomasetti recommended moving the towers some 60m (200ft) to the southeast due to poor soil conditions. Friction

The publicly accessible skybridge sits 170m (558ft) above ground level.

piles were sunk in the new location and concrete mats were poured above them. The twin towers rose above this foundation simultaneously, the job having been awarded to two separate contractors, both skilled in concrete construction. The towers climbed at a rate of up to two floors per week, meaning that they were completed in three short years – and have been symbols of the city and the country ever since.

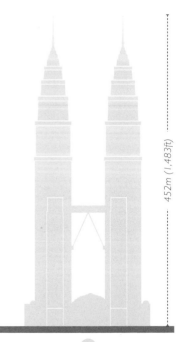

452m (1,483ft)

Each spire is made up of 23 segments and topped by a ring ball comprised of 14 rings.

The two 88-storey towers have 197,500 sq m (2.13 million sq ft) of floor area.

The towers' façades are made of 33,000 stainless steel and 55,000 glass panels.

Brazilian landscape architect Roberto Burle Marx designed the mall's roofscape and the adjacent park, which are considered his last works and were completed after he died in 1994.

OASIA HOTEL DOWNTOWN

LOCATION: Singapore | COMPLETION: 2016 | HEIGHT: 191m (626ft)
STOREYS: 27 | PRIMARY FUNCTIONS: Hotel, offices | OWNER/DEVELOPER:
Far East Organization | ARCHITECT: WOHA | STRUCTURAL ENGINEER:
KTP Consultants | KEY FACTS: The world's largest green façade.

Building Green

WOHA – the firm of Richard
Hassell and Wong Mun Summ – has
explored the integration of vertical
vegetation in increasingly ambitious
projects. The Oasia Hotel Downtown
– which occupies the southern half of
a green space made up of lawn and
mature trees – replaces the green area
it took away with its planted façade
and sky gardens. WOHA calculate
the success of this approach with
what they call the 'green plot ratio',
where 100 per cent represents a 1:1
replacement. Here, they claim a ratio
of 1,100 per cent – the equivalent of
11 stacked parks.

The building's outer façade is made
up of 25,490 sq m (274,372 sq ft) of
aluminium mesh panels covered in 21
species of creepers planted in 1,793
fibreglass tubs. These 'screens of green'
are accentuated by the aluminium's
five shades of red, from pink to dark
ruby. Hidden behind the façade
are weathertight, painted precast
concrete panels.

Sky Gardens

The second contributor to the green
plot ratio is the trio of multistorey sky
gardens at floors 6, 12 and 21. These
generously scaled spaces, open on
two sides, alternate as they ascend,
giving each façade one or two large
'windows' onto the city. At the 27th
floor is a roof garden with pool, capped
by an oculus about 35m 115ft) above
the top floor.

Functions

The tower stacks two main functions
above the five-storey base's lobby and
parking area: integrated hotel–office
spaces occupy levels 7 to 11, while
starting at level 12 is the Oasia brand
hotel. Each function is housed in
narrow, L-shaped plans overlooking
the sky gardens. The use of gardens
eliminates the need for a central core,
so WOHA pushed this element to
the four corners, creating blank walls
which become a canvas for the
biggest green façade in the world.

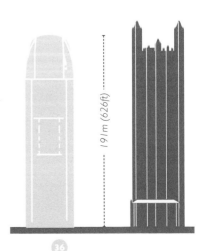

191m (626ft)

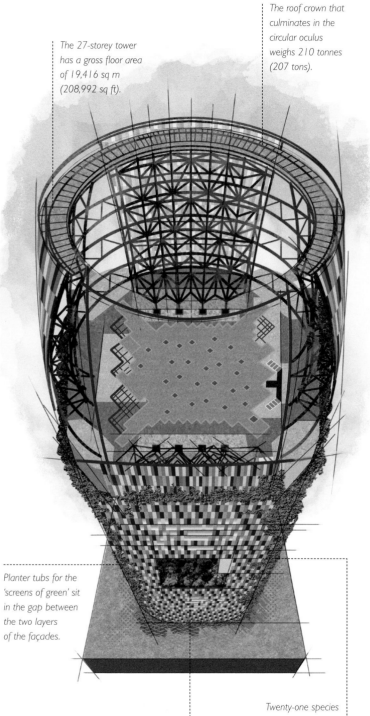

The 27-storey tower has a gross floor area of 19,416 sq m (208,992 sq ft).

The roof crown that culminates in the circular oculus weighs 210 tonnes (207 tons).

147

Planter tubs for the 'screens of green' sit in the gap between the two layers of the façades.

Twenty-one species of creepers grow in the 1,793 large fibreglass tubs.

The 30m (98ft) high outdoor sky gardens are like huge windows onto the city.

BITEXCO FINANCIAL TOWER

LOCATION: Ho Chi Minh City, Vietnam | **COMPLETION:** 2010 | **HEIGHT:** 262.5m (86 ft) | **STOREYS:** 68 | **PRIMARY FUNCTION:** Offices | **OWNER/ DEVELOPER:** Bitexco Group, Bitexco Land | **ARCHITECTS:** Carlos Zapata Studio, AREP Ville | **STRUCTURAL ENGINEER:** Leslie E Robertson Associates (LERA) | **KEY FACTS:** Features the first cantilevered helipad in Vietnam and one of the highest such in the world.

Bitexco Group

Founded in 1985, the Bitexco Group quickly expanded from a firm solely focused on textiles to a multi-industry corporation, with interests in shopping malls, mineral water, real estate and the energy sector. Its national and global ambitions find suitable expression in the tower bearing its name in Ho Chi Minh City's historic district. Since its inauguration on 31 October 2010, Bitexco Financial Tower has been included in lists of the world's most striking skyscrapers.

Design Concept

Much of the attention is due to the building's form, which architect Carlos Zapata modelled on the bud of a lotus, the national flower of Vietnam. The glass tower rises from the street with a plan shaped like a rhombus, where the four sides are slightly convex and the corners are rounded.

A leaf-like façade appears to wrap the tower's north side, while a helipad projects from the opposite side. The exterior walls lean outwards slightly up to the 22nd floor, after which they lean in all the way to the top with its triangular plan and concave façade above the helipad.

Helipad

Another focus of attention is, obviously, the helipad, a feature commonly sited atop towers but here cantilevering out from the 52nd floor. The round helipad juts asymmetrically from the southeastern side of the tower's rhombus-shaped plan, as if to gesture toward the nearby Saigon River. With the conical glass projection below and the triangular section above it, the helipad integrates with the building's form to make the lotus design concept explicit.

The cantilevered helipad is located 191m (627ft) above street level.

BUILDING AND STRUCTURE

Function

Most of the tower is taken up by office space, including Bitexco Group's own offices, but it also includes five storeys of retail in a podium, three levels of underground parking, an observation deck on level 49, restaurants on levels 50 and 51 and a VIP lounge next to the helipad. Double-decker elevators serve the office floors, while express lifts run directly to the observation deck.

Façade

Glass curtain walls are treated with various screen-printed patterns to cut down on direct sunlight. Inside, wooden louvred shutters allow for further sun protection and add a traditional touch to the modern design. The slightly convex sides of the tower are covered in flat panes of glass, though curved glass is used at the more strongly rounded corners.

Structure

Challenges to the structural design started at the base, where the soil conditions (the site is on an alluvial plain) led the structural engineers to sink the piles down 75m (246ft) and provide a concrete mat foundation at the second of four subterranean levels. The reinforced concrete substructure consists of the core walls, perimeter columns and flat-plate floor slabs. Concrete outrigger trusses and belt walls between pairs of perimeter columns stiffen the tower against wind forces, which are high considering the low-scale surroundings of the tower. The only use of steel framing in the building occurs at the helipad, which is supported by a pair of cantilevered girders 25m (82ft) long. Secondary beams cantilever out from the girders to support the circular edges of the helipad and helicopters weighing up to 2.7 tonnes (2.65 tons).

The podium contains approximately 10,000 sq m (107,600 sq ft) of retail and conference facilities and restaurants.

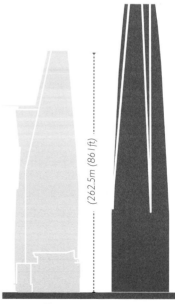

(262.5m (861ft))

37

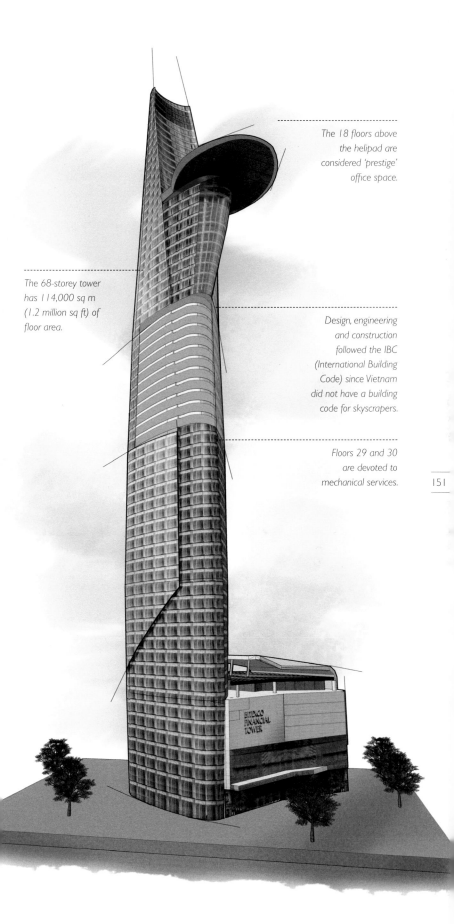

The 18 floors above the helipad are considered 'prestige' office space.

The 68-storey tower has 114,000 sq m (1.2 million sq ft) of floor area.

Design, engineering and construction followed the IBC (International Building Code) since Vietnam did not have a building code for skyscrapers.

Floors 29 and 30 are devoted to mechanical services.

151

BITEXCO FINANCIAL TOWER

CANTON TOWER

LOCATION: Guangzhou, China | **COMPLETION:** 2010 | **HEIGHT:** 604m (1,982ft) | **STOREYS:** 37 | **PRIMARY FUNCTIONS:** Telecommunications, observation | **OWNER/DEVELOPER:** Guangzhou New TV Tower Co., Ltd. **ARCHITECTS:** Information Based Architecture (IBA), Guangzhou Design Institute | **STRUCTURAL ENGINEER:** Arup | **KEY FACTS:** The tallest structure in China when completed; at time of writing, the second tallest after Shanghai Tower.

Competition

Although they include some of the tallest structures in the world, television towers are historically more engineering than architecture, more utility than beauty. When Mark Hemel and Barbara Kuit of Amsterdam's IBA were invited to enter a 2004 competition for a broadcast tower in Guangzhou (formerly known in English as Canton), they aimed for the opposite: one that was curved and, in their own words, 'sexy'. They won the competition by wrapping the facilities in a pinched and twisting diagrid structure made of a web of steel columns, ring beams and diagonal bracing.

Mixed Uses

While the terms of the competition also included the design of an 18-hectare (44-acre) park and a master plan for the 57-hectare (40-acre) surroundings, the tower itself features more than just broadcasting facilities. It also has indoor and outdoor observation desks, a 4-D cinema, exhibition spaces, rotating restaurants in four intermittent enclosures and an outdoor 'Spider Walk'. The two-storey base is connected to a subway and underground parking, while the tower is topped by a slanted Ferris wheel ('Bubble Tram') and a 'Sky Drop' thrill ride. The exterior diagrid cloaks these elements, so from a distance they are invisible, but up close they are objects that appear to float within the web.

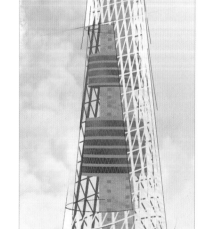

A walkway spiralling around the core ascends from the roof of a mini 'building' at 170m (558ft) to an elevation of 350m (1,148ft).

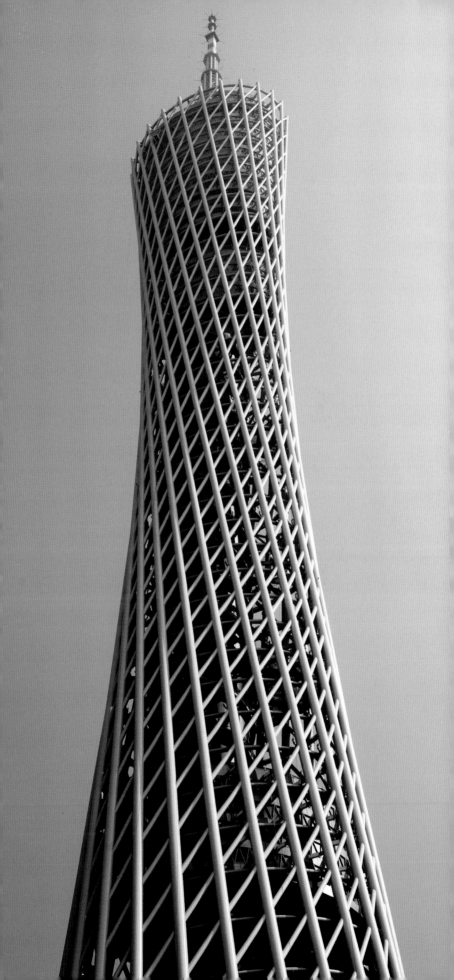

BUILDING AND STRUCTURE

Structure

The diagrid's elliptical plan changes from a large ellipse at the base to a small one at the top that is rotated about 90 degrees. Three elements comprise the concrete-filled steel structure: first, a series of 25 straight columns that lean as the tower twists and taper from a diameter of 2m (6½ft) at the base to 1.1m (3½ft) at the top; second, 75cm (2½ft) diameter ring beams behind the columns that slope at about 15 degrees from horizontal; and third, 75cm (2½ft) diagonals that are in line with the columns and span from one column–ring-beam node to the next. The floors for the four multistorey enclosures have their own supporting structure, made up of rectangular steel sections that span from the diagrid to the elliptical core. Since the ring beams lean at 15 degrees, the floors are connected at the columns so their loads are directly transferred to these vertical members.

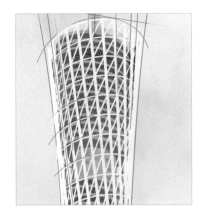

A tuned mass damper at 438.4m (1,438ft) stabilizes the tower against strong winds.

Lastly, the mast, which adds 150m (492ft) to the tower, was fabricated atop the building in two parts, with the top portion made inside the wider base and jacked into place in May 2009. Canton Tower was completed in October 2010 in time for the Asian Games, when fireworks shot from the structure.

Construction

To erect the approximately 450m (1,476ft) tall diagrid, four cranes were positioned outside its footprint and another inside; a third of the way up, three of the outside cranes were removed. The concrete core – its footprint consistent from bottom to top – was poured with the aid of a sliding formwork. The diagrid's prefabricated steel followed: first the columns and nodes, then the ring beams, then finally the diagonals. When six levels of steel were in place, the columns were lined and filled with concrete. All connections were bolted initially, then welded and the bolt connections burnt off, resulting in a seamless lattice.

604m (1,982ft)

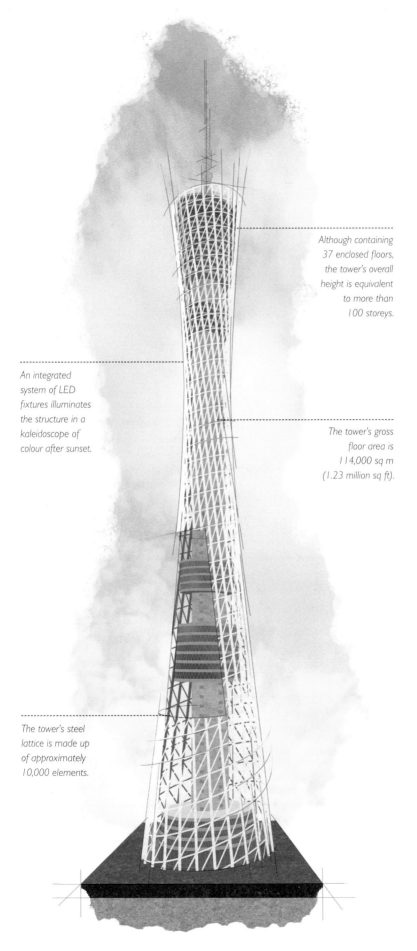

Although containing 37 enclosed floors, the tower's overall height is equivalent to more than 100 storeys.

An integrated system of LED fixtures illuminates the structure in a kaleidoscope of colour after sunset.

The tower's gross floor area is 114,000 sq m (1.23 million sq ft).

The tower's steel lattice is made up of approximately 10,000 elements.

BANK OF CHINA TOWER

LOCATION: Hong Kong, China | COMPLETION: 1990 | HEIGHT: 367m
(1,205ft) including masts | STOREYS: 72 | PRIMARY FUNCTION: Offices
OWNER/DEVELOPER: Bank of China Hong Kong | ARCHITECTS: I M Pei
& Partners, Kung & Lee Architects | STRUCTURAL ENGINEERS: Leslie E
Robertson Associates (LERA); Valentine, Laurie, and Davis | KEY FACTS:
First building outside the United States to reach over 305m (1,000ft).

Historical Context

Plans for the Bank of China's new office building in the centre of Hong Kong began in 1982, two years before the signing of the Sino-British Joint Declaration, which detailed the handover of the former British colony of Hong Kong back to China in July 1997. The tower – the tallest in the city, and in all Asia when first completed – took on special significance in this context. That the tower was designed by Hong Kong-born American architect Ieoh Ming Pei was hardly a coincidence – his father, 89 years old in 1982, was a former head of the Bank of China.

Site

Although the location, between affluent Victoria Peak to the south and Victoria Harbour to the north, guaranteed some prominence to the 72-storey skyscraper, the immediate site was a difficult one: an island ringed by highways and ramps on three sides. I M Pei provided a car drop-off on the high, north end of the site, with gardens and fountains on the east and west cascading down to a lower plaza and a second entrance, for pedestrians, on the south.

On this 'island', Pei designed a three-storey granite base from which the glass and aluminium tower appears to grow.

Building Form

Pei envisioned the tower like a bamboo shoot, as if advancing with every stage of growth. He did this by diagrammatically stacking and setting back five 13-storey modules, starting with a square at the base and removing one triangular chunk at each module – at floors 25, 38 and 51. Instead of spiralling, the pieces taken away move from north to west to east, ending in double-stacked triangular modules on the south side. Angular rooflines occur at each setback, giving the tower an origami-like appearance.

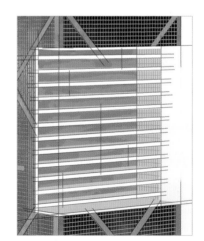

The faceted plans mean the cores are pushed away from the centre towards the sides.

BUILDING AND STRUCTURE

Structure

The triangulation of the tower is seamlessly integrated with the structure, which uses large diagonal steel members to transfer vertical and lateral loads to four concrete megacolumns – one at each corner of the square plan. (The fifth column in the centre transfers its load to the corners at the large atrium spanning from the 19th to 25th floors.) The hybrid structural design by engineer Leslie E Robertson uses about half as much steel as a traditional office tower, while it capably addresses the typhoon-force winds that can batter the city.

Complications

Although a lasting symbol of Hong Kong and its independence, Pei's design created a couple of issues: the gradual removal of triangular sections eliminated the possibility of a central core (the top sections have a core that is not aligned with the floors below); and the initial expression of horizontal steel members was read as a series of unpropitious X-shapes by *feng shui* experts (the removal of the horizontals satisfied them).

Façade

The skyscraper has an almost cartoon-like appearance of vertical and diagonal lines thanks to Pei's façade treatment, which features a relentless grid of reflective glass panes surrounded by oversized aluminium covers that accentuate the large structural members. These metal lines are illuminated at night, 'painting' the structural forces on the skyline.

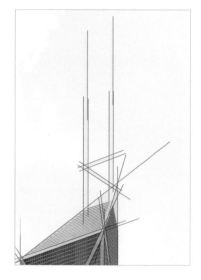

The pair of antennae adds about 80m (262ft) to the height of the building beyond its top floor.

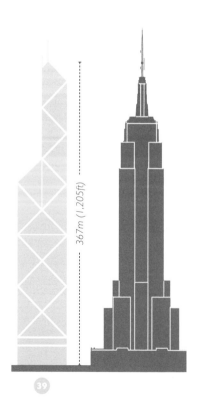

367m (1,205ft)

39

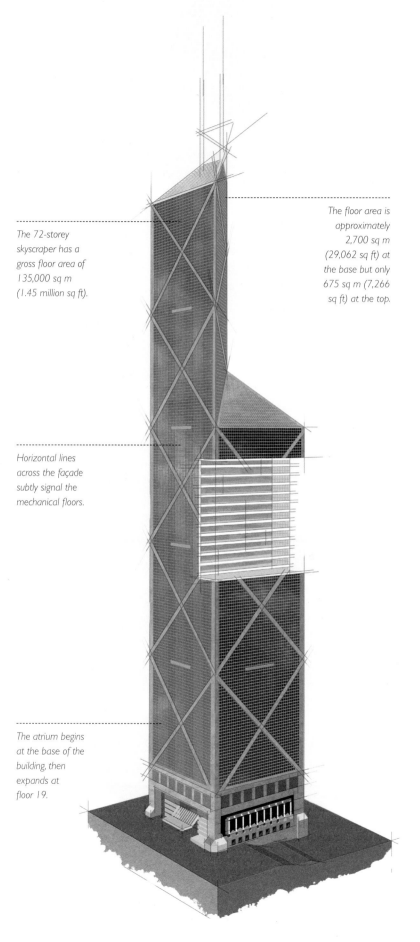

The 72-storey skyscraper has a gross floor area of 135,000 sq m (1.45 million sq ft).

The floor area is approximately 2,700 sq m (29,062 sq ft) at the base but only 675 sq m (7,266 sq ft) at the top.

Horizontal lines across the façade subtly signal the mechanical floors.

The atrium begins at the base of the building, then expands at floor 19.

CCTV HEADQUARTERS

LOCATION: Beijing, China | **COMPLETION:** 2012 | **HEIGHT:** 234m (768ft)
STOREYS: 54 | **PRIMARY FUNCTION:** Offices | **OWNER/DEVELOPER:** China
Central Television (CCTV) | **ARCHITECTS:** Office for Metropolitan
Architecture (OMA), East China Design & Research Institute (ECADI)
STRUCTURAL ENGINEERS: Arup, ECADI | **KEY FACTS:** Received Council
on Tall Buildings and Urban Habitat (CTBUH) Best Tall Building
Worldwide Award in 2013. Its façade was completed in 2008 in time for the
Olympics, but the building was not officially completed until 2012.

Design Overview

If such a thing as an anti-skyscraper
skyscraper exists, this is it. When
Rem Koolhaas, founder of Rotterdam's
OMA, was vying for the commission
for the headquarters of China Central
Television (CCTV) in 2002, he
described skyscrapers as banal, a type
that had not seen any innovation
since the completion of New York's
Twin Towers in 1972. Instead of a
single tower soaring to record-book
numbers in Beijing's central business
district, Koolhaas proposed a closed
loop, resembling a thickened Möbius
strip, that would connect and
facilitate the process of making and
broadcasting TV, culminating in a
75m (246ft) cantilever positioned
200m (656ft or 37 storeys) above
street level.

Function

US architect Louis Sullivan applied
his famous phrase 'Form ever follows
function' to tall buildings through the
tripartite organization of base (retail),
middle (offices) and top
(mechanical). Although Koolhaas
departed from historical precedents
with his closed loop, he could not get
away from a tripartite composition,

given that the CCTV Headquarters
is made up of three volumes: the
nine-storey plinth (including a three-
storey basement), two towers and the
fourteen-storey overhang. The plinth
houses the large production studios,
the two leaning towers contain
offices and spaces for research and
editing, and the overhang is devoted
to administration. All three volumes
add up to 473,000 sq m (5 million
sq ft) – 15 per cent more floor area
than the Twin Towers.

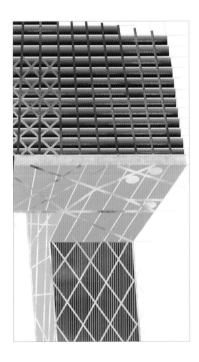

*The linking level between the two towers
features 4m (13ft) wide glass floors
allowing visitors to peer down a 162m
(530ft) drop.*

BUILDING AND STRUCTURE

Structure

The success and feasibility of skyscrapers are enabled by structural engineering, but Koolhaas's departure from formal precedent equated to a partial abandonment of decades of applied knowledge in the engineering of tall buildings. Cecil Balmond of Arup, a frequent collaborator of Koolhaas, was forced to be innovative. He responded with a steel-framed, braced-tube system comprising a regular grid of columns and edge beams plus patterned diagonal bracing, the latter expressed as steel sections cutting across the glass façades – one of the design's most memorable features. Far from regular, the spacing of the diagonal bracing expresses the forces working on the building: dense where forces are high (such as at the corners) and open where they are less (at the roof).

Seismic Considerations

Before ground could be moved, the unprecedented design had to be proved seismically sound, given Beijing's location in an earthquake zone. To do so, a 7m (23ft) scale model of the structure built out of copper (which closely equates with steel's ductility) was subjected to a 'shaking table' – thanks to its robust braced-tube system, it passed easily.

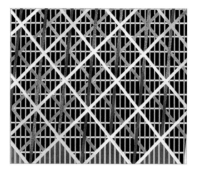

Detail of the steel frame and braced-tube construction system, with steel squares cutting across the glass façade.

Construction

The 113,000 tonnes (111,000 tons) of steel framing are anchored to raft foundations 7m (23ft) deep that are supplemented by 33m (108ft) piles beneath the towers. During construction the core, external structure and concrete floors grew floor by floor, just like any skyscraper, but joining the towers required very careful planning. Engineers had to monitor any movement of the structure, make any adjustments to the linking elements and then specify that the connection be made early in the morning, before the rising sun caused the steel to expand. At 8:00 on a cold winter's morning the daring building closed its loop, making its mark on the Beijing skyline ever since.

234m (768ft)

The usable floor area comes to 473,000 sq m (5 million sq ft).

The shape has been described as a 'Z crisscross', a 'twisted doughnut' and 'the pants'.

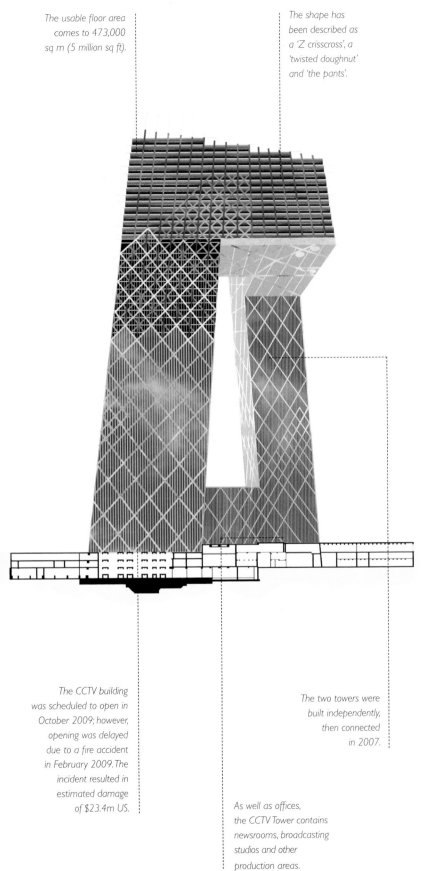

163

The CCTV building was scheduled to open in October 2009; however, opening was delayed due to a fire accident in February 2009. The incident resulted in estimated damage of $23.4m US.

The two towers were built independently, then connected in 2007.

As well as offices, the CCTV Tower contains newsrooms, broadcasting studios and other production areas.

SHANGHAI WORLD FINANCIAL CENTER

LOCATION: Shanghai, China | COMPLETION: 2008 | HEIGHT: 492m (1,640ft) | STOREYS: 101 | PRIMARY FUNCTIONS: Hotel, offices | OWNER/ DEVELOPER: Shanghai World Financial Center Co., Ltd. | ARCHITECTS: Kohn Pedersen Fox Associates (KPF), Mori Building Company, Irie Miyake Architects and Engineers; East China Architectural Design & Research Institute (ECADI), Shanghai Modern Architectural Design (Group) STRUCTURAL ENGINEERS: Leslie E Robertson Associates (LERA), Arup KEY FACTS: The tallest building in China when completed. Council on Tall Buildings and Urban Habitat (CTBUH) Best Tall Building Overall for 2008.

Site History

Shanghai World Financial Center (Shanghai WFC) is the second of three towers planned for the Lujiazui Financial District in Shanghai's Pudong New District on the eastern bank of the Huangpu River. The completion of each tower, starting with Skidmore, Owings & Merrill's Jin Mao Tower in 1999, resulted in a new tallest building in China. In the case of KPF's Shanghai WFC, the ambition for a nearly 500m (1,640ft) tall tower came only after foundations had been built for a shorter tower – making for a challenging structural redesign.

Mixed Uses

From its early planning by Mori Building Company and KPF in 1993, Shanghai WFC included offices, as would be expected in the area, but also a mix of cultural, entertainment, hospitality and recreation facilities. The latter were important since they were lacking in Pudong, which had become the commercial and financial heart of Shanghai – and indeed all of China.

Building Form

Both the initial and final designs of the Shanghai WFC start from a square at the base and culminate in a slender hexagon rotated 45 degrees at the peak. This form 'draws' two arcs in a V-shape across two façades, and results in a tapered profile on the perpendicular sides. The wide top was punctuated by a circular opening in the original design, but in response to concerns that the shape evoked Japan rather than China, the form changed to an easier-to-build trapezoid.

At 474m (1,555ft), the observation 'bridge' was the tallest in the world when completed in 2008.

BUILDING AND STRUCTURE

Foundations

Foundation work for the initial design commenced in 1997 and was completed the following year, after which the project was put on hold due to the Asian financial crisis. The substructure consists of about 200 concrete-filled steel-pipe friction piles driven 78m (256ft) into the ground and capped at 17.5m (58ft) below ground for a mat and basement floors in concrete. This foundation was designed for a tower 460m (1,509ft) tall, but in 1999, when the project came back, the client decided to grow the building to its final height and add 16 per cent more floor area.

New Structure

Although Arup had performed conceptual structural designs for the original tower, Leslie E Robertson's firm was responsible for devising a suitable structure for the taller tower. They determined that the foundation could accept a larger building if its weight were decreased by 10 per cent. To achieve this, the engineers focused on reducing the thickness of the core's concrete walls. The best route was to increase the stiffness of the perimeter walls through the creation of a megastructure consisting of megacolumns at the corners, diagonal bracing, belt trusses and, at three levels, outrigger trusses connecting the megacolumns to the core.

Façade

The strong steel-and-concrete composite structure is barely glimpsed behind the reflective glass façade, but it is the clear glass enclosure of the 100th-floor observation deck that draws more attention. It sits above – and via glass floors gives vertiginous views of – the Sky Gate, the skyscraper's most striking feature and a key component in reducing the lateral forces acting upon it.

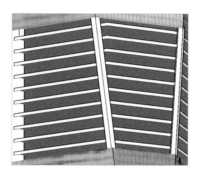

Six megacolumns are located at each corner of the hexagonal floors in the tower's midsection.

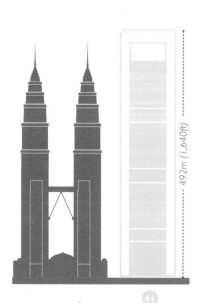

492m (1,640ft)

41

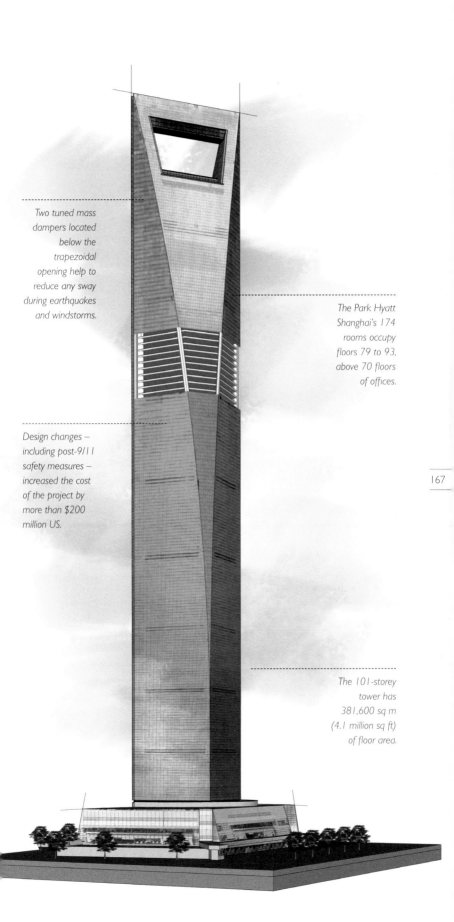

Two tuned mass dampers located below the trapezoidal opening help to reduce any sway during earthquakes and windstorms.

The Park Hyatt Shanghai's 174 rooms occupy floors 79 to 93, above 70 floors of offices.

Design changes – including post-9/11 safety measures – increased the cost of the project by more than $200 million US.

167

The 101-storey tower has 381,600 sq m (4.1 million sq ft) of floor area.

SHANGHAI TOWER

LOCATION: Shanghai, China | **COMPLETION:** 2016 | **HEIGHT:** 632m (2,073ft) | **STOREYS:** 128 | **PRIMARY FUNCTIONS:** Offices, hotel | **OWNER/ DEVELOPER:** Shanghai Tower Construction & Development **ARCHITECTS:** Gensler, Tongji Architectural Design (Group) **STRUCTURAL ENGINEERS:** Thornton Tomasetti, Tongji Architectural Design (Group) **KEY FACTS:** The tallest building in China and the second tallest in the world. Twenty-one atriums are stacked in the tower.

Site History

Shanghai Tower is the third of three towers planned as early as 1990 for the city's Lujiazui Financial District, which was previously farmland on a peninsula formed by a bend in the Huangpu River. Each successive tower gained height and forward-thinking principles: the Jin Mao Tower (1999) was designed by Skidmore, Owings & Merrill to recall historic pagoda forms; Kohn Pederson Fox's Shanghai World Financial Center (2008; page 164) used abstract symbolism in the tapered form pierced by a trapezoidal opening; while Gensler's megatall structure (buildings over the height of 600m/1,969ft qualify) pushed the envelope in numerous ways.

A Vertical City

Gensler won a 2007 competition for Shanghai Tower with a design that prioritized sustainability and community. The skyscraper's smooth skin belies what is conceptually nine stacked zones, each one 12 to 15 storeys tall; the architects were inspired by small-scale courtyards in Shanghai and aimed to recast them vertically. From bottom to top, there are retail and conference facilities in the first zone, five zones of offices, two hotel zones and a top zone for the highest non-enclosed observation deck in the world. The office and hotel floors overlook three vertical gardens at the base of each zone; these atriums sit in the expanse between two layers of glass to give the occupants pleasant places to meet, eat lunch or grab a cup of coffee high above the city streets.

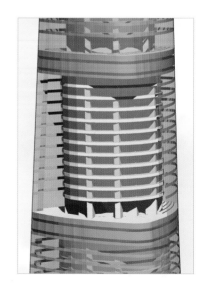

The cylindrical floor plates are set back at each zone to give the tower its tapered form.

BUILDING AND STRUCTURE

Façade

In plan, the two layers of glass are circular (inner) and triangular (outer), the latter with rounded corners like a guitar pick. The generous gap between the two vertical surfaces ranges from 60cm (2ft) at the middle of the triangles' edges to 10m (33ft) at the corners. The outer skin of clear glass – 20,589 panels with more than 7,000 unique shapes – is hung from cantilevered trusses at the two-storey mechanical and refuge floors between the zones. With such large spans between the two curtain walls, the outer wall is stabilized by struts and, at the rounded corners, cross-bracing. The latter enables a notch to be made at one corner, which accentuates the tower's twisting, tapering form.

Structure

The notch may appear to be purely architectural, but it is structural: it works with the 120-degree clockwise rotation to minimize wind loads – cutting them by as much as 24 per cent, which saved the client millions of dollars due to the reduced size of the structure. Further lateral stability comes from the central rectangular core, whose concrete walls are attached to eight concrete-filled steel megacolumns (two per side) via steel outrigger trusses at the mechanical floors, where double belt trusses, also in steel, tie the columns together. These columns – aligned with the tiered inner curtain wall so they do not interfere with the atriums – are supplemented with 45-degree corner megacolumns at the lower floors, while the top of the tower includes a five-storey-tall, 900-tonne (886-ton) tuned mass damper (made

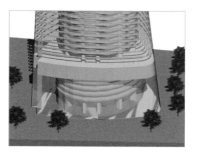

The tower connects to the subway, parking and its neighbours underground.

with copper, magnets and steel plates) which counteracts the sway caused by high-altitude winds. The tower's 128 floors are supported by a concrete mat 6m (20ft) deep and more than 1,000 concrete and steel bore piles – a strong foundation for this stacked, sustainable city.

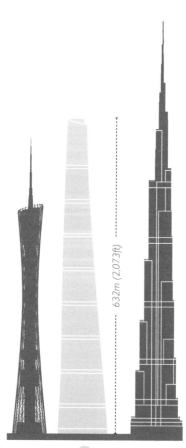

632m (2,073ft)

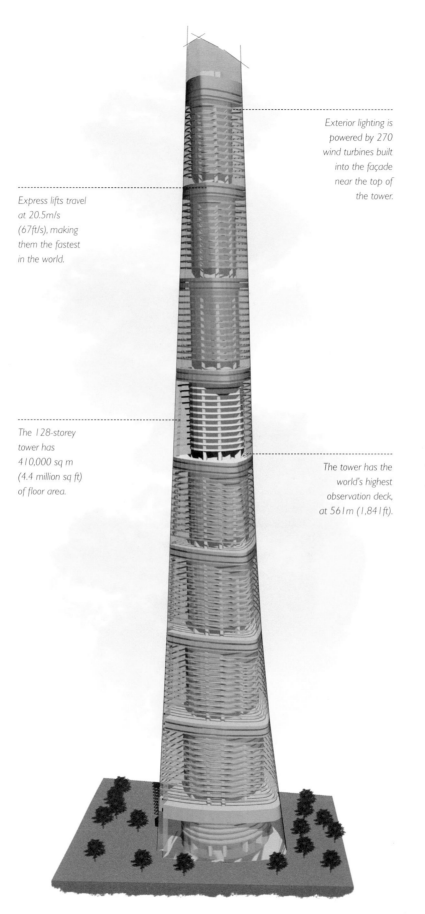

Exterior lighting is powered by 270 wind turbines built into the façade near the top of the tower.

Express lifts travel at 20.5m/s (67ft/s), making them the fastest in the world.

The 128-storey tower has 410,000 sq m (4.4 million sq ft) of floor area.

The tower has the world's highest observation deck, at 561m (1,841ft).

TAIPEI 101

LOCATION: Taipei, Taiwan | COMPLETION: 2004 | HEIGHT: 508m (1,667ft) | STOREYS: 101 | PRIMARY FUNCTION: Offices | OWNER/ DEVELOPER: Taipei Financial Center Corporation | ARCHITECT: C Y Lee & Partners | STRUCTURAL ENGINEERS: Evergreen Consulting Engineering, Thornton Tomasetti | KEY FACTS: The tallest building in the world from 2004 until 2010.

Lucky 8

In Chinese cultures, the luckiest number is 8, combinations of this number are particularly auspicious. It is no wonder that the tallest tower in Taiwan (officially the Republic of China) is based on eights. Most prominent are the eight eight-storey sections that make up the bulk of the skyscraper that is the centrepiece of Taipei's Xinyi District.

Traditional Precedents

These flared sections, which sit between the 25-storey battered-wall base and the 10-storey-tall spire, recall traditional Chinese pagodas, which could be considered as premodern skyscrapers, some of them reaching 100m (330ft) and towering over their surroundings. Each stacked section of these mostly wooden structures moves independently, which makes them resistant to the earthquakes and typhoon-force winds that periodically batter the region.

Ornament

Although Taipei 101's profile is instantly recognizable, it is not made up solely of such large-scale gestures. C Y Lee and C P Wang, the heads of C Y Lee & Partners, designed ornamental touches in stainless steel that ground the design in tradition while accentuating the tower's form. These include *ruyis* (ancient symbols recalling clouds) atop each eight-storey section, dragon-like figures at the corners and huge coins where the eight sections meet the base.

Taipei 101 was the first tower to reach more than 500m (1,640ft).

BUILDING AND STRUCTURE

Structure

Although Taipei 101's structure is rigid, its expressive and recognizable design is a response to Taiwan's extreme seismic and tropical storm conditions as well as its difficult geology. The latter was dealt with by means of 380 bored piles extending 60m (200ft) to bedrock through layers of soft, silty clay. Above the piles is a reinforced concrete mat more than 3m (10ft) thick, while two slurry walls surround the 101-storey tower and the six-storey, L-shaped podium to prevent groundwater from entering the five basement levels.

The steel and composite structure above the foundation is made up of a central braced core connected to perimeter 'supercolumns' through outrigger trusses; the whole makes up a so-called 'megaframe'. Reiterating the lucky number, the core is framed with 16 columns, while the number of supercolumns is eight, two to each side of the square plan. The outrigger trusses are full-floor, located at the bottom of each eight-storey section, with further trusses distributed in the base. Roughly the bottom two-thirds of the structure is composite, where the columns were boxed out with steel plates and filled with concrete.

Damper

The substantial structural megaframe cannot address all of the lateral forces acting upon the building, so the tower incorporates a massive tuned mass damper at the 88th floor.

Each eight-storey section inclines inward seven degrees at the perimeter.

Made of welded steel plates which are attached to an array of dampers and hydraulic shock absorbers, the 590-tonne (580-ton) pendulum converts kinetic energy to thermal energy in order to reduce the amount of sway during strong winds and earthquakes. Not something to be hidden away, this golden orb is visible to visitors to the tower's observation deck and rooftop restaurant.

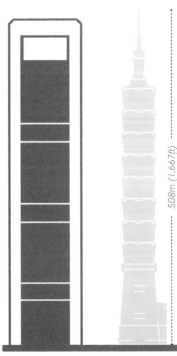

508m (1,667ft)

43

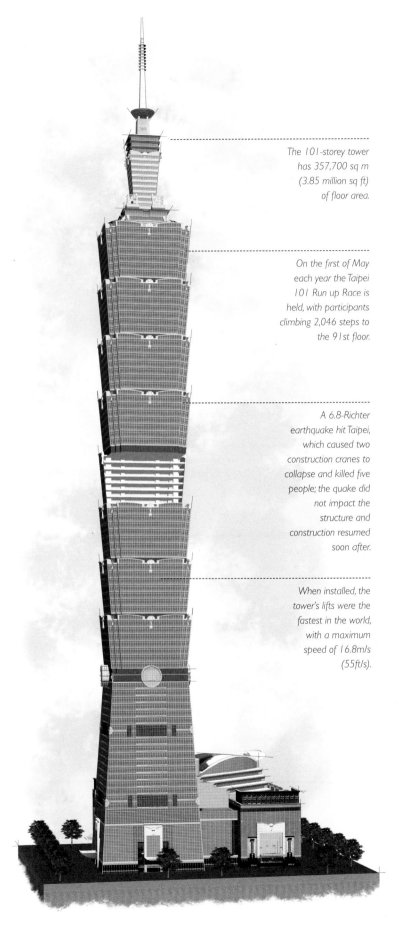

The 101-storey tower has 357,700 sq m (3.85 million sq ft) of floor area.

On the first of May each year the Taipei 101 Run up Race is held, with participants climbing 2,046 steps to the 91st floor.

A 6.8-Richter earthquake hit Taipei, which caused two construction cranes to collapse and killed five people; the quake did not impact the structure and construction resumed soon after.

When installed, the tower's lifts were the fastest in the world, with a maximum speed of 16.8m/s (55ft/s).

LOTTE WORLD TOWER

LOCATION: Seoul, South Korea | COMPLETION: 2017 | HEIGHT: 555m (1,819ft) | STOREYS: 123 | PRIMARY FUNCTIONS: Hotel, offices | OWNER/ DEVELOPER: Lotte Engineering and Construction | ARCHITECTS: Kohn Pedersen Fox Associates (KPF), Baum Architects | STRUCTURAL ENGINEERS: Leslie E Robertson Associates (LERA), Chang Minwoo Structural Consultants | KEY FACTS: Fifth-tallest building in the world at its completion.

Asian Supertalls

This century, much of the attention lavished on skyscrapers is directed towards China, which is, as of 2017, home to nearly 50 supertall buildings over 300m (984ft). On the other hand, South Korea – a country which admittedly has only one per cent of the landmass of China – has only three supertalls. The tallest of these is Lotte World Tower, which entered the world rankings as the fifth-tallest building when it was completed in early 2017.

Lotte

Lotte is one of South Korea's largest conglomerates and is best known for chains of hotels, shopping malls and amusement parks. One of the latter – Lotte World – opened in 1989 in Seoul's Jamsil tourist zone and is considered the world's largest indoor theme park. It is also just across the street from the new Lotte World Mall (also by KPF), which consists of a shopping mall, a cinema, a concert hall and an aquarium in an 11-storey podium as well as Lotte World Tower. The tower contains offices, so-called 'officetels' (small apartments with hotel amenities for the use of office workers), a 260-room luxury hotel and a glass-walled observation deck, among other secondary functions, stacked across its 123 floors from bottom to top.

Lotte's attempt to go vertical – and upscale – faced its share of difficulties. Most notably, it took 15 years to obtain a building permit, which was given on condition that the conglomerate paid to reconfigure a nearby runway so military planes would not be in danger of hitting the tower on approach.

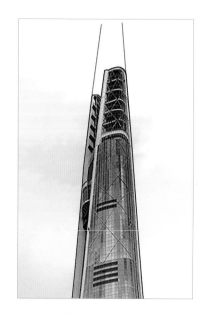

A steel diagrid supports the upper floors of the tower, including the section that extends about 57m (186ft) beyond the roof.

BUILDING AND STRUCTURE

Building Form

The tower's simple, aerodynamic form belies its internal complexity, which is claimed to house more than a dozen different functions. The tower rises fairly straight from its square plan to about the top of the office floors, from which it gradually tapers to the lantern extending well past its roof. Like the much earlier John Hancock Center in Chicago (page 24), KPF's tapered form makes sense with regard to its innards: deep floor plates are a logical choice for offices but not for officetels or hotels.

In plan, two corners of the square are curved, while the other two are recessed. This effect is created by wrapping two L-shaped curtain walls with vertical fins around the plan but holding them apart where they would otherwise meet. These two recessed seams widen as the tower rises, culminating in a distinctive, sizable gap at the lantern. The observation deck projects from the seam below the lantern to give stomach-churning views through its glass floor – the highest such observatory in the world.

Structure

The supertall skyscraper sits upon a 6.5m (21¼ft) thick concrete mat – requiring 5,000 truckloads of concrete – that rests on 1m (3¼ft) diameter piles to prevent settlement. The superstructure consists of reinforced-concrete core walls, eight concrete megacolumns (two each side) with steel perimeter columns between them, two sets of three-storey-tall steel outriggers, and two sets of three-storey-tall steel belt trusses.

The numerous bands of mechanical floors are visible on the façade through the horizontal stripes.

The floors comprise concrete and metal deck on steel beams up to level 86, and flat concrete slabs above. The megacolumns are capped at that point; steel perimeter columns and beams are used above. An exposed steel diagrid supports the lantern, which forms an elegant apex to the country's tallest tower.

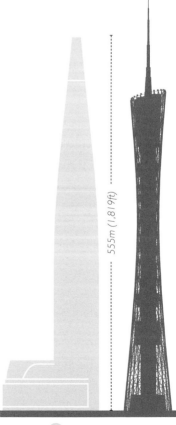

555m (1,819ft)

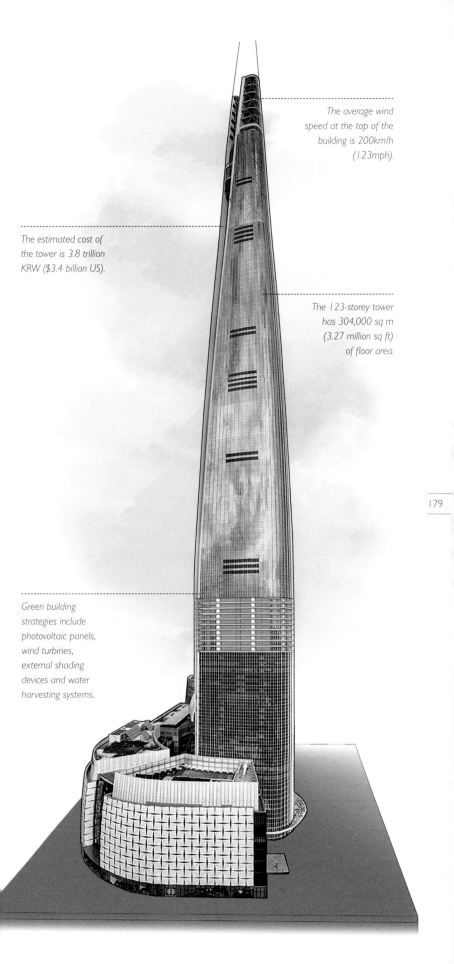

The average wind speed at the top of the building is 200km/h (123mph).

The estimated cost of the tower is 3.8 trillion KRW ($3.4 billion US).

The 123-storey tower has 304,000 sq m (3.27 million sq ft) of floor area.

179

Green building strategies include photovoltaic panels, wind turbines, external shading devices and water harvesting systems.

MODE GAKUEN COCOON TOWER

LOCATION: Tokyo, Japan | **COMPLETION:** 2008 | **HEIGHT:** 204m (668ft)
STOREYS: 50 | **PRIMARY FUNCTION:** Education | **OWNER/DEVELOPER:**
Mode Gakuen | **ARCHITECT:** Tange Associates | **STRUCTURAL ENGINEER:**
Arup | **KEY FACTS:** The tallest educational building in Japan and the
second-tallest educational building in the world.

Vertical Campus

'Cocoon' is an apt label for this building in Tokyo's busy Shinjuku district: The bulging tower looks as though it is wrapped in silk. Inside are three vocational colleges stacked one on top of the other, including, appropriately enough, a fashion school. 'Cocoon' also works as a metaphor for nurturing the students within and preparing them for their post-college lives, when they will 'grow their wings and fly away'.

The Mode Gakuen Cocoon Tower is located close to Shinjuku Station, the busiest railway station in Tokyo, if not the world. Given the area's building density and high property values, there was no choice but to build the colleges as a vertical campus. Together the three schools operated by Mode Gakuen – Tokyo Mode Gakuen (fashion), HAL Tokyo (information technology) and Shuto Ikō (medical care) – have a capacity of 10,000 students within the 50-storey tower.

Plan

Although the tower's form and façade look like a ready-made icon, the plan strongly determined the project's appearance. Designed by Paul Tange, son of the famous Kenzō Tange, each floor is given over to three rectangular classrooms that are spaced apart and rotated 120 degrees in the circular plan. In between are three-storey student lounges with east, southwest and northwest views through curved expanses of glass, and in the middle is the Y-shaped core, each leg of which provides a set of elevators for one of the three schools.

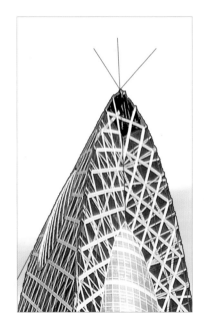

The diagonal bracing extends over the top of the tower to enclose the rooftop services and complete the 'cocoon' metaphor.

BUILDING AND STRUCTURE

Curved Form

Rather than extrude the rectangular classrooms and curved lounges straight up, Tange tapered the tower at both ends to provide more landscaping and create a distinctive top for the Cocoon. An eight-storey-tall, egg-shaped volume with two auditoriums, retail and underground parking is connected to the tower at ground level (the main entrance is between tower and 'egg'), while large elliptical windows punctuate the top floors of the classrooms.

The three-storey lounges provide smaller-scale communal spaces within the vertical campus.

Structure

The main structure of the tower, as designed by Arup, is composed of two systems: three elliptical diagrid frames at the classrooms and an inner core made up of 12 concrete-filled steel-tube columns (two pairs of columns for each leg of the core). Further, the glass walls at the lounges are supported by double-arched Vierendeel trusses connected to the steel diagrids. To resist the seismic forces prevalent in the region and the rotations in the midsection caused by the tower's form, viscous dampers were installed at the inner core – six per floor from the 15th to the 39th. Due to the complex column layout, the tower sits atop a 3.8m (12½ft) thick raft slab that in turn rests on cast-in-place concrete piles.

Roof

Mode Gakuen's distinctive top presented a couple of functional challenges, for helicopter access and window washing. The latter is accommodated by a central turntable, Y-shaped rails and openings in the façade that allow a gondola hanger to protrude where needed. Above that is a retractable helipad that, in the event of an emergency, can be opened within eight minutes by a pair of hydraulic jacks. These pieces are hidden behind the silky façade from which the students will eventually emerge.

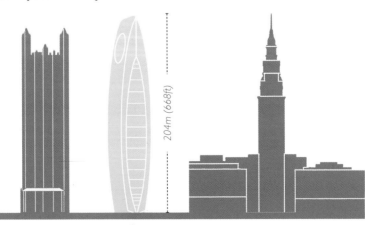

204m (668ft)

The 'cocoon's' glass façade is printed with adhesive film strips that echo the name of the tower and also shade the interior.

The 50-storey tower has 80,065 sq m (870,425 sq ft) of floor space.

The vertical campus of three schools is served by a cogeneration (combined heat and power) plant inside the building.

183

Given the rotation of the plan, it is nearly impossible to see more than one vertical band of student lounges at any one time.

Q1 TOWER

LOCATION: Gold Coast, Australia | **COMPLETION:** 2005 | **HEIGHT:** 323m (1,058ft) | **STOREYS:** 78 | **PRIMARY FUNCTION:** Residential
OWNER/DEVELOPER: Sunland Group, Surfers Paradise Beach Resort
ARCHITECTS: Sunland Group, The Buchan Group, Innovarchi
STRUCTURAL ENGINEERS: Arup, Whaley Consulting Group | **KEY FACTS:**
The world's tallest residential tower from completion until 2011.
The tallest building in Australia.

Gold Coast

Gold Coast, in southeastern Queensland, is one of the largest urban areas in Australia apart from the major state capitals, and it is a consistently popular tourist and leisure destination. With at least 100 buildings over 20 storeys, Gold Coast is definitely a built-up city, yet one that is billed as the theme-park capital of Australia. The resort city's tall buildings are almost exclusively residential and Q1 Tower is the tallest of them all.

Queensland Number One

Located in the high-rise suburb of Surfers Paradise, Q1 is the creation of Iranian developer Soheil Abedian, whose Sunland Group developed, designed and built the project. Innovarchi, the firm of architects Stephanie Smith and Ken McBryde, designed the substantial retail podium. The project was conceived in 2000, the year of the Sydney Olympics, so it drew inspiration from that city's famed opera house and the swooping design of the Olympic torch. Olympic references run deep: Q1 refers to Queensland Number One, Australia's sculling team from the Games in the 1920s.

Building Form

The footprint of Q1 Tower reportedly occupies only 10 per cent of its site, with the rest taken up by gardens, waterfalls, pools, a spa, dining areas and the open-air retail galleria. The last draws visitors into the tower and frames an upward view of it through a glass roof. The tower plan is like an ellipse that has been trimmed at one end: a concave side faces Surfers Paradise Boulevard to the west, while two convex sides converge towards the beach and ocean on the east.

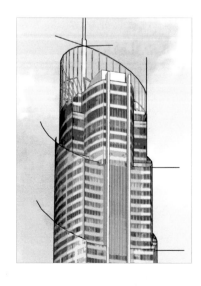

The difference between the tip of the tower and the highest occupied floor (the observatory on 77) is 88m (288ft).

BUILDING AND STRUCTURE

Crown

The strongest allusion to the Olympic torch is found at the top of the tower, where a public observatory on the 77th floor provides views from Byron Bay to Brisbane. Here a glass roof frames views up to the angled crown, a decorative feature of steel and glass that sweeps up towards the 93.5m (307ft) stainless-steel spire. Daring souls wishing to get a closer look at this element can brave the SkyPoint Climb, a walkway added in 2010 that ascends alongside the sloping glass walls to a height of 270m (886ft).

Façade

The elliptical tower's glass curtain wall has a striped appearance, thanks to its articulation of insulated clear glass panes alternating with white spandrel panels. As the tower rises, concentric curves of curtain wall that appear to overlap each other fall away just below the top. Their angled tops echo the tower's angled crown, which directs one's gaze to the tall spire.

Structure

The tower sits upon 26 concrete piles 2m (6½ft) in diameter that extend 40m (131ft) into the ground and are anchored to 4m (13ft) of solid rock. The superstructure is a reinforced concrete frame with perimeter columns connected to the core through concrete blade walls. The design's aerodynamic form reduces the wind forces acting on the tower – but stay away from the SkyPoint Climb on windy days.

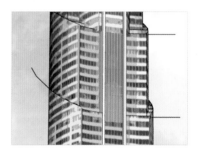

Level 60 – 180m (590ft) above the street – has a 30m (98ft) tall indoor sky garden.

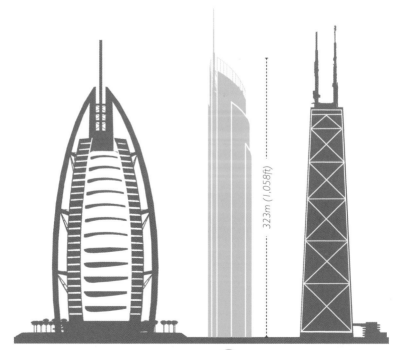

323m (1,058ft)

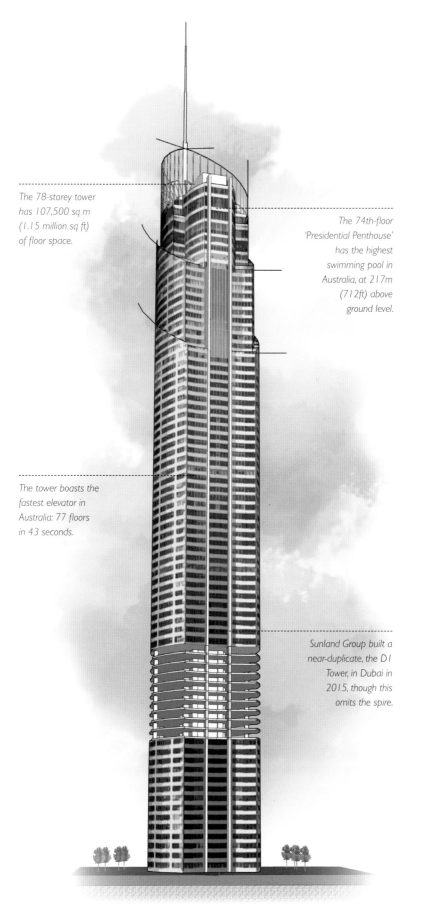

The 78-storey tower has 107,500 sq m (1.15 million sq ft) of floor space.

The 74th-floor 'Presidential Penthouse' has the highest swimming pool in Australia, at 217m (712ft) above ground level.

The tower boasts the fastest elevator in Australia: 77 floors in 43 seconds.

Sunland Group built a near-duplicate, the D1 Tower, in Dubai in 2015, though this omits the spire.

GLOSSARY

atrium: a large, multistorey enclosed space, usually in the centre of a building's plan.

Beaux-Arts: a classical architectural style promoted in the late 19th century by the École des Beaux-Arts in Paris.

below grade: below ground level.

belt truss: a truss that wraps the perimeter of a building, somewhat in the manner of a belt, in order to stiffen the overall structure.

braced-tube system: a perimeter structural frame that resists lateral forces by the introduction of diagonal bracing.

bundled-tube system: a series of perimeter frames that are tied together (such as by belt trusses) to resist lateral forces.

butt-glazing: a glass-to-glass joint on an exterior curtain wall that uses structural silicone and interior mullions to obtain a flat external appearance.

caisson: a reinforced concrete structure below grade that is formed by pouring concrete into a hollow form, usually of cylindrical steel; used to support a skyscraper's columns.

cantilever: a horizontal projection, such as a balcony or cornice, supported at one end only.

catenary arch: an arch that resembles an inverted catenary – the curve formed by a uniformly loaded chain or rope suspended from two points.

clear span: a span not interrupted by intermediate elements, such as columns.

core: the central stem of a building, made up of vertical services (stairs, elevators, mechanical shafts, etc.) and structural elements (steel framing or concrete walls).

cornice: a projection at the top of a building; traditionally used to keep rain away from the exterior wall, but in modern times purely decorative.

curtain wall: a non-load-bearing wall, often of glass and metal, applied in front of a structural frame to keep out water and provide the main expression of a tower.

deck(ing): the form, often made from corrugated metal, upon which reinforced concrete slabs are poured.

diagrid: a load-bearing structure made of diagonal steel grids; an increasingly popular means of addressing vertical and horizontal loads in tall buildings in this century.

double-loaded corridor: a central corridor with rooms on both sides.

floor plate: see *slab*.

gunite: a mixture of cement, sand and water that is forced through a pressure hose to coat vertical or angled surfaces.

hat truss: an interior truss atop a building that connects elements of a structural system together.

lateral force: any horizontal force acting upon a building, e.g. wind, earthquake, hurricane; see also *loads*.

loads: the forces acting upon a building in the horizontal (building mass, people and other 'live loads', gravity) and vertical (earthquake, wind) directions that structural engineers need to address.

mechanical floor: a storey devoted to mechanical equipment, such as boilers, chillers, generators and pumps; most towers have several, including one at roof level.

megacolumn: a column made up of multiple members, often in composite (steel and concrete).

megatall: a skyscraper that exceeds 600m (1,968ft) in height.

oculus: a circular opening in a wall or in the apex of a dome.

outrigger: a system, such as a truss, that ties together two structural systems, usually the core and the perimeter frame.

pilotis: columns at the base of a building that elevate the first level and open the ground floor.

portal brace: an opening consisting of a beam and two columns that is made rigid by adding diagonal members near the top corners.

post-tensioned: (referring to reinforced concrete) prestressed by tensioning (pulling) reinforcing rods after the concrete has hardened.

prestressing: applying forces to a structure to deform it so it will withstand loads more effectively and without deflection; post-tensioned concrete is a widely used method.

reinforced concrete: concrete that is strengthened through the addition of steel bars, wire mesh or other.

riser: a vertical shaft in a core to accommodate pipes and other essential services.

setback: in zoning, a portion of a building positioned away from a street, pavement or property line, usually to preserve sunlight in the public sphere.

settling/settlement: downward movement of a structure due to its weight and the composition of the ground beneath it.

shear wall: a structural wall that serves to counter lateral forces, such as wind and earthquakes; also called 'blade wall'.

sheet-pile wall: a construction of wood, steel or concrete driven inground below grade to resist lateral pressure of water and earth; often located at a tower's perimeter and inserted before the excavation of the earth inside.

sky garden: an elevated green space, often enclosed, that introduces nature and fresh air into the upper floors of a skyscraper.

sky lobby: an elevated storey where users transfer from a lower elevator to an upper one or vice versa; a means of stacking elevators in a single shaft.

slab: the construction of a floor, often of reinforced concrete and metal decking resting on structural steel.

slip form: concrete formwork that is slowly raised vertically in a continuous process as the concrete is poured and sets.

slurry wall: a foundation wall, similar to a sheet-pile wall, that is made by excavating a trench, filling it with slurry, inserting reinforcing, and then filling it with concrete as the slurry is pumped out.

smoke tower: a vertical shaft through a skyscraper that ventilates smoke in the event of a fire.

soffit: the underside of a horizontal element; distinct from a ceiling.

spandrel: the part of a curtain wall that conceals the columns and/or the edges of slabs.

stack effect: the pull of warm air upwards through a vertical space, such as an atrium.

substructure: any part of a tower's structure below grade.

superstructure: any part of a tower's structure above grade.

supertall: a skyscraper that exceeds 300m (984ft) in height.

topping off: a construction milestone marking the completion of a building's superstructure.

truss: a structural element or framework formed of triangular sections for the sake of rigidity.

tuned mass damper: a heavy object located near the top of a skyscraper that is 'tuned' to the building to reduce any lateral sway during high wind and earthquakes.

vertical load: see *loads*.

Vierendeel truss: a truss made with top and bottom chords connected rigidly by vertical components, often at the scale of one or more storeys.

viscous dampers: hydraulic devices that dissipate energy during earthquakes; often used in concert with a tuned mass damper.

zoning: a jurisdiction's legal code that controls the size and/or character of buildings.

INDEX

ACKNOWLEDGEMENTS

Thanks to everybody at RotoVision (Abbie Sharman, Emily Angus, Stephen Haynes) for trusting in me to write this book and then making it happen every step of the way.

Thanks to Philip Beggs and Robert Brandt, whose illustrations make this book stand out among the many titles devoted to skyscrapers.

Thanks to Chicago's Council on Tall Buildings and Urban Habitat and New York's Skyscraper Museum for their ongoing research, exhibitions and other publicly available materials devoted to tall buildings; without their thorough and passionate work, writing this book would have been an insurmountable task.

And thanks, as always, to my wife, Karen, and daughter, Clare, for supporting me through another one of my writing projects.

IMAGE CREDITS

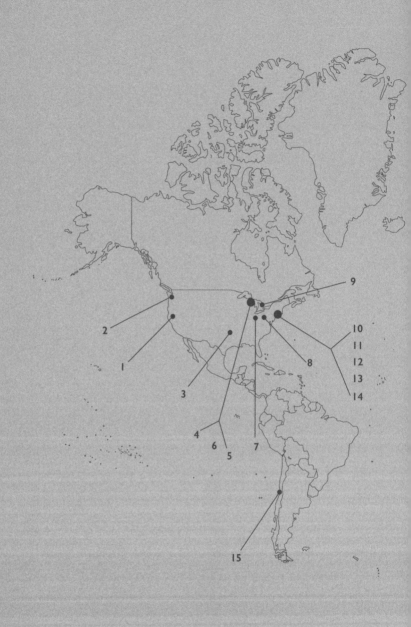

10 19 32 18 23 4 16 29 2 9 20 24 36 8 45 7 3 25 40 28 11 27 17 2